The Narrow Margin

Directed by: Richard Fleischer
Screenplay by: Earl Felton

An Andrew *Velez Book*

FREDERICK UNGAR PUBLISHING CO.
New York

Published by arrangement with RKO General, Inc.

PUBLISHER'S NOTE:

This is the complete final screenplay for the RKO film.
The movie as released may differ from the screenplay
in some respects.

Copyright 1952 by RKO Radio Pictures, Inc.

Copyright renewed 1980 by RKO General, Inc.

Printed in Great Britain
by Biddles of Guildford

ISBN 0-8044-6135-X

INTRODUCTION

Through the years since its release in 1952 *The Narrow Margin* has gained a well-deserved reputation as a small gem of the hardboiled genre. This 71-minute black-and-white sizzler was one of the brighter cinematic contributions from RKO in what proved to be a very troubled year for the studio. Directed by Richard Fleischer from a skillful screenplay by Earl Felton (based on a story by Martin Goldsmith and Jack Leonard), a solid cast was headed by Charles McGraw and Marie Winsor.

Set on a train bound from Chicago to Los Angeles, the film introduces Charles McGraw as the hostile police protector of the gangster's widow, played in classically tough style by Marie Winsor. She is scheduled to testify before a grand jury on the West Coast. The trio of gangsters sent to kill her are not certain which of the passengers is their target. (The early working title for the film was *The Target*).

Skillfully integrated into the plot are a number of surprises. The tough moll widow, for whom the cop has only contempt, turns out to have another identity, which becomes known only late in the adventure. The twists in character and plot are typical of the *noir* film viewpoint. It is an unstable world in which surface realities are deceptive. A "good" cop who is killed in an ambush while protecting the widow is revealed to have a somewhat tarnished shield. A passenger on the train who exudes an ominous presence is actually a train company detective. A little boy who is a passenger is convinced the policeman is actually a burglar. The moral structure of the characters is relative.

Travelling on a train has been successfully used as a device in a number of films. Hitchcock's *Stranger on a Train* and *North by Northwest*, as well as *Human Desire, The Manchurian Candidate*, and *Tall Target* are some of the more successful films. None, however, achieved to the same degree the sense of confined space so convincingly captured in *The Narrow Margin*. Director Fleischer continued to be particularly adept in handling crime and suspense dramas—*Violent Saturday* (1955), *Compulsion* (1959), and *The Boston Strangler* (1968). His results with other subjects have been mixed. *20,000 Leagues under the Sea* (1954) has become something of a perennial adventure favorite, and *Fantastic Voyage* (1966) is an imaginative fantasy film. By contrast, *Barabbas* (1962), *Dr. Dolittle* (1967), and *Che!* (1969) were costly and elephantine embarrassments, failures both critically and financially.

Illustrating that less can sometimes be more, *The Narrow Margin* was produced at a negative cost of $230,000 and became one of the best sleepers in the company's history. Its success was especially meaningful in a year that found the studio embroiled in a number of lawsuits and burgeoning problems. Among the suits was one brought by Paul Jarrico, a veteran screenwriter and a victim in the McCarthy witchhunt. He sued RKO for refusing to give him a credit on *The Las Vegas Story*.

Later in the year, perhaps in part as a result of the problems he faced in running the company, Howard Hughes, then head of RKO, attempted to sell his stock to a syndicate of buyers. Three of the syndicate's members were revealed shortly thereafter to have unsavory connections. A minority stockholders' suit followed. During the final five months of 1952 not a single film went into production and the studio lost a number of valuable members of its creative staff, including producer Jerry Wald and writer-producer Norman Krasna. The net loss financially for the year was over $10 million. Less than half of the films that RKO released were full-fledged productions of its own studio.

During the year, other studios released films that included *Singin' in the Rain, High Noon, Limelight, Five Fingers*, and *Viva Zapata*. From abroad came *The Lavender Hill Mob, The Winslow Boy*, and *Breaking the Sound Barrier* (all from England), and *Rashomon* (from Japan). *This Is Cinerama* was one of the continuing parade of films utilizing novel technical achievements in hopes of luring back to the movie theatres an audience that was staying at home to watch television. Other 1952 RKO releases included Howard Hawks's *The Big Sky* and Fritz Lang's *Clash by Night*. The latter offered the public one of its early viewings of Marilyn Monroe in a significant role.

More than thirty years after its original release, *The Narrow Margin* has outlasted many of the spectacular and successful releases of the year. It remains today an engrossing and flavorful film of character and action.

Andrew Velez

CAST:

Walter Brown	Charles McGraw
Mrs. Neil	Marie Windsor
Ann Sinclair	Jacqueline White
Tommy Sinclair	Gordon Gebert
Mrs. Troll	Queenie Leonard
Kemp	David Clarke
Densel	Peter Virgo
Gus Forbes	Don Beddoe
Jennings	Paul Maxey
Train Conductor	Harry Harvey

CREDITS:

Screenplay	Earl Felton
Story	Martin Goldsmith and
	Jack Leonard
Producer	Stanley Rubin
Director	Richard Fleischer
Director of Photography	George E. Diskant, A.S.C.
Art Directors	Albert S. D'Agostino
	Jack Okey
Set Decorations	Darrell Silvera
	William Stevens
Film Editor	Robert Swink
Sound	Francis Sarver
	Clem Portman

THE NARROW MARGIN
(TARGET)

FADE IN

RAILROAD BLOCK SIGNAL—NIGHT
The pattern of lights changes and the semaphores move. A train whistle sounds and camera tilts down as a locomotive bursts from under a bridge, rushing towards us in a beam of dazzling light. The screen explodes with smoke and steam and we superimpose the title:

"T A R G E T"

DISSOLVE
A blur of lighted windows as the streamlined coaches whip past; then more titles and credits. Swimming out of the montage, a railroad track marker begins to fill the screen. It reads:

"CHICAGO YARD LIMIT"

DISSOLVE

INTERIOR CHICAGO RAILROAD STATION—NIGHT

Along platform as the train creeps in, slowing. Rain glistens on the coaches and we hear the hollow mechanical voice of the announcer:
ANNOUNCER: ... Central Pacific train ten, the 49'r from Los Angeles, arriving track three, etc ...
Camera holds on the open door of one of the Pullmans and we introduce Gus Forbes standing here, a dead cigar clamped in his mouth; behind him is Walter Brown. Red Caps are running forward. The airbrakes sigh. And now the train stops, Forbes and Brown stepping to the platform, each carrying a suitcase, dodging baggage trucks. Forbes sets his bag down, strikes a match on the side of the car and lights up.
FORBES: You handle the bags. I'll meet you at the taxi stand.
He exits off as Brown hails a Red Cap.
BROWN: Red Cap...! *(indicating bags)* These two right here.
RED CAP: Yessir. You going on east or staying over?
BROWN: Neither. We're going back tonight. *(shows him tickets)* Golden West Limited—for Los Angeles.
RED CAP: *(surprised)* That train leaves in a hour, sir.
BROWN: *(impatiently—gives him a tip)* Yeah, I know. Make sure our stuff's aboard.
The Red Cap begins scribbling numbers off ticket envelope.
RED CAP: That's car ten, rooms A and B.
He gives Brown back the ticket envelope and picks up the bags, exiting, as Brown strides off.

DISSOLVE

EXTERIOR CHICAGO RAILROAD STATION—NIGHT
At Taxi Stand—A cab is just pulling up to the curb where Gus Forbes is waiting. He tightens his rather seedy overcoat around his neck as the taxi starter opens the door.
FORBES: *(entering cab)* There's another passenger coming. Hold it.

INTERIOR TAXI—NIGHT
Forbes sinks into the back seat and we observe him for a moment—a man of fifty, as well worn and comfortable-looking as

his coat, he seems mellowed. His eyes are almost kindly, but they are the kind that miss nothing, except the ashes spilled on his lapel. The cigar has gone dead again and he lights it as Brown comes along curb, Forbes leaning forward to open the door. Brown climbs in and Forbes raps on the front panel of glass. The driver slides it back.

FORBES: 9417 Water Street, South.

BROWN: And if you know any short cuts, take 'em, driver.

The driver notes address on pad, Brown closing panel.

FORBES: *(placidly)* Relax, Walter, we'll make it okay.

The cab starts. Brown glances at his wrist watch.

BROWN: *(unconvinced)* If we don't, I know a couple of suitcases that're going to get plenty lonesome.

Forbes chuckles, spilling ashes on his coat.

EXTERIOR CHICAGO LOOP—NIGHT (STOCK)

Under the Elevated—The taxi forges ahead through the jam of traffic and we hear the jumbled sounds of horns, police whistles and the thunder of the "L" overhead.

INTERIOR MOVING TAXI—NIGHT (PROCESS)

Brown is lighting a cigarette. Forbes, hands folded contentedly across his middle, is sucking on the dead cigar. His eyes are half closed.

BROWN: Your cigar's dead.

He holds the match under Forbes' cigar.

FORBES: *(puffing)* Thanks. I'm thinking of changing brands—something with a self-starter on it. *(cocks an eye at Brown)* I'll bet you're wondering the same thing I am. What she looks like.

Brown flicks the match out.

BROWN: *(shortly)* I don't have to wonder. I *know.*

FORBES: *(mock surprise)* Why, that's wonderful, Walter. Nobody's seen her but *you* know what she looks like. What a gift!

BROWN: Come off it. You're just making talk.

FORBES: Maybe, but we'll get there just as fast talking. What about this dame, Mr. Crystal Ball?

Brown grins, crushing out his cigarette.

3

BROWN: A dish.

FORBES: What kind of a dish?

BROWN: The sixty-cent special. Cheap, flashy and strictly poison under the gravy.

FORBES: Amazing. And how do you know all this?

BROWN: Well, she was married to a hoodlum, wasn't she? So what kind of a dame marries a hood?

FORBES: *All* kinds.

BROWN: Gus, at heart you're a boy scout.

> *He grins at Forbes amused. Forbes grunts, looking at Brown with real affection.*

FORBES: Maybe it's just old age coming on. *(smiles)* Anyhow, I've got five bucks says you're wrong this trip. What can I lose?

BROWN: Five bucks. You're on. *(peers out taxi window)* Slightly out of the high rent district, isn't it?

> *Forbes follows his gaze as the taxi makes a turn.*

EXTERIOR CHICAGO STREET—NIGHT

A cheerless avenue of brownstone fronts thrown into harsh relief by a corner arc light. Pools of water have formed in the chuck holes and a gust of wind ripples the puddles, sending a cardboard box tumbling end over end across the street in a rising cloud of papers and refuse. The taxi splashes unevenly through the ruts, passing several parked cars. Save for these and the figures of two pedestrians walking, hunched over against the wind, the street is deserted and the lights in the houses are few and dim.

INTERIOR MOVING TAXI—NIGHT (PROCESS)

Forbes scrunches around, looking through rear window.

FORBES: Nobody tailed us.

BROWN: You *hope.*

> *The cab stops, Forbes opening door.*

EXTERIOR CHICAGO STREET—NIGHT

As Forbes and Brown alight, appraising the unlovely exterior of 9417—a depressing three-story trap with steps leading up from the sidewalk to doorway. The wind howls and the naked branches

4

of a tree throw weaving shadows on the face of the building. A single light burns over the vestibule.

FORBES: *(to cab driver)* Wait for us—and douse your lights, will you? *The driver nods, pulling his collar tighter around his neck as he shuts off headlights and engine. Forbes and Brown mount the steps.*

INTERIOR BROWNSTONE APARTMENT—NIGHT
Shooting from hallway—Forbes and Brown pause outside; then open the door, entering. Just inside the entrance are several mailboxes and Forbes checks these. He turns, indicating a rickety staircase which hugs the wall, extending up. The hall continues back and is lost in gloom. Over shot we hear the sighing of the wind and the muffled sing-song music of a phonograph playing a popular tune. The sound comes from upstairs.

BROWN: *(grins, glancing up)* Want to double that bet?

FORBES: *(ignores this)* Number ten. Upstairs.

Brown ascends the stairs, Forbes following, the stairs creaking under their feet. Camera tilts up to second floor landing where Brown turns, waiting in the uncertain light until Forbes joins him.

Medium shot—upper hallway. The two men proceed to a door halfway down the hall. This is #10. The sound of the music grows louder. Forbes knocks, but the music continues. He knocks again and a man's voice is heard:

MAN'S VOICE: *(behind door)* Who is it?

FORBES: Forbes.

A lock rattles and the door opens against a chain-stopper. Bill Wilson, a Chicago plainclothesman, looks out in the shaft of light, appraising his visitors. He is holding a revolver and his shoulder holster is exposed against his shirt sleeves.

FORBES: *(continued)* It's okay.

He palms a badge in his hand, holds it out.

INTERIOR ROOM—NIGHT
Reverse angle through door. We see the L. A. Detective badge in Forbes' hand.

5

FORBES: *(indicating Brown)* This is Detective-Sergeant Brown. *(as Wilson slips the chain off)* What's the music for—a welcome?

WILSON: *(opening door)* You don't know *how* welcome.

The camera pulls back as Forbes and Brown enter, Wilson swinging the door wide and putting his gun back in the holster. He then closes the door, bolts it, turning.

WILSON: *(continued)* Hey, turn that thing off! Your escort's here.

Camera pans away from Brown and Forbes and across the room we find Mrs. Neil, a woman of about twenty-eight who stands before a portable phonograph with a record in her hand. There is a quick impression of blonde hair and, as she turns, we see the sexy, petulant mouth and sense her hard, insolent manner. She tosses the hair out of her eyes, shuts off the phonograph and stares boldly at the newcomers, drawing on her cigarette.

WILSON: *(continued)* Forbes and Brown. Los Angeles.

MRS. NEIL: How nice—and how's Los Angeles? *(appraising them closer)* The sunburn wear off on the way out?

Brown tries to catch Forbes' eye, but the latter is crossing to the phonograph.

FORBES: If you don't mind, we're a little short of time, Mrs. Neil. Our train leaves in half an hour.

He starts to close lid of phonograph.

MRS. NEIL: *(sharply)* Just a minute! I can pack my own things. First I'd like to know who I'm going with.

FORBES: You're going with us.

MRS. NEIL: Don't be too sure of that. How do I know you're cops?

Brown and Forbes exchange looks.

BROWN: *(grins)* Was I right?

FORBES: Don't rub it in. I owe you five.

Wider angle. Forbes grimaces ruefully as Wilson comes over from closet, slipping into his topcoat.

WILSON: Better show her your orders. She's afraid of a trap.

MRS. NEIL: You bet I am. Getting killed sort of runs in our family. They got Frankie—and his widow's next! I'm taking a big chance.

Forbes shrugs, pulls out an envelope and hands it to her.

FORBES: Okay, that's the D.A.'s signature. *We're* taking a big chance, too. If we don't get you to the coast it'll cost us our jobs.

6

Mrs. Neil: *(scanning paper)* You're breaking my heart.

Brown: *(coming over)* Satisfied?

Mrs. Neil: All right, I'll get my things together. *(to Wilson)* So long, mother.

She crosses to couch as Forbes stoops, picking up newspapers from floor.

Wilson: *(buttoning up coat)* Have a nice trip. *(to Brown and Forbes)* She's all yours, boys.

Wilson shakes hands with Brown, walks to door, Brown following to unbolt it. Wilson exits, Brown locking door after him. Mrs. Neil is packing a small suitcase. The camera moves closer to table as Forbes picks up a copy of the Chicago Star, leaving another copy face up, the headlines showing:

"CRACK DOWN ON LOS ANGELES CRIME!"
"POLICE HUNT MOBSTER FRANKIE NEALL'S
PAY-OFF LIST!"

Brown comes over to table and shuts the phonograph lid.

Closer at couch, where Mrs. Neil is pressing her knee against the top of a bulging suitcase as Forbes strolls into scene, holding the paper.

Forbes: *(reading aloud)* "Rumor grand jury to hold special session—hint slain gang lord's widow may testify in graft probe." Huh! *(folds paper, studying her)* Word gets around, doesn't it?

Mrs. Neil: That's what's worrying me.

She snaps a catch down as Forbes strikes a match.

Forbes: *(innocently)* Frankie carry any life insurance, Mrs. Neil?

Mrs. Neil: *(short of breath)* Quit hinting.

Forbes is watching her with interest.

Forbes: *(lighting cigar)* Oh I thought he might've left you an annuity—not cash exactly, but something just as good. Like that pay-off list they talk about.

She gives him a scorching look, snaps lock closed on suitcase.

Mrs. Neil: I heard you the first time. *(straightens)* You'd like a look at that list, wouldn't you?

Closeup—Forbes.

Forbes: *(casually, grins)* I always like to feel I'm in on the know. I buy a paper, first thing I turn to is Winchell.

MRS. NEIL: *(puts out cigarette in tray)* I'll read it off to you sometime.
She smiles insolently at Forbes who smiles back, puffing his cigar.
FORBES: When?
MRS. NEIL: *(too sweetly)* When the grand jury asks me and not before. So quit making a pest of yourself—*(grabs suitcase away from him)*—and keep your hands off my baggage!
BROWN: *(impatiently)* Come on, let's get out of here.
MRS. NEIL: *(glaring at Forbes)* I'm ready.
She flounces ahead with her suitcase, grabbing her coat off the chair and carrying it, camera pulling back as Brown glances around the room, turns off the table lamp. Forbes sighs heavily and walks to door where Mrs. Neil is waiting. He unbolts the lock, opens it motioning Mrs. Neil to proceed.
MRS. NEIL: *(continued)* After you.
Forbes bows, exits, Brown coming over to click off the other lights and follow Mrs. Neil into the hall.
Medium shot—upper hallway as Brown comes out, closes door and joins Forbes and Mrs. Neil at head of stairs, pausing to help her into her coat.
Closer shot—favoring Brown and Mrs. Neil whose face appears tense and drawn. As Mrs. Neil buttons her coat, she accidentally breaks a string of large beads. She manages to grab them all, except for one bead which drops to floor, rolls off landing to floor below, camera tilting down as bead comes to rest next to a man's shoe. From our higher camera position we are unable to observe his face—only a hat pulled low over his face and a fur-lined overcoat. The man, Eddie Densel, is holding a gun and, as the stairs begin creaking, he backs away down the hall.
An angle from bottom of stairs as Mrs. Neil and Brown follow Forbes down the stairs. As Forbes reaches the bottom, he pauses to strike a match to his dead cigar. The woman and Brown are directly behind him, but out of Densel's sight, who is flattened against the wall some distance back in hall.
Reverse from Densel's angle. Densel raises the gun, waiting, but Mrs. Neil and Brown are not in sight from this position. Forbes, his cigar lighted, throws the match away and starts down the last step, Brown taking Mrs. Neil's arm. Densel lifts the gun higher—

but at this moment a door suddenly opens behind him, light spilling out. *Camera trucks backwards.* Forbes whirls as does Densel and we see an elderly tenant coming out of his room. Quickly, Forbes hurls his weight against Mrs. Neil, who collides with Brown. Densel, momentarily off guard, fires at the spot where Mrs. Neil was standing. Forbes ducks, drawing his own gun. Densel fires twice more. Forbes' gun goes off in the air and he topples forward, Brown fighting his way past Mrs. Neil, who is screaming. Densel is already racing for the back door. The tenant, who has dropped to his knees, gets up. Brown pounds down the hall, but Densel has already gone out the door.

EXTERIOR BROWNSTONE—NIGHT
The day's wash is hanging on lines strung across the yard. Densel, running madly from the house, disappears behind a line of sheets. A moment later Brown races out after him, plunging into the flapping laundry. There is a loud clap of thunder and the scene flickers to lightning as the wind whips wildly at the wash. Travelling shot—Brown. He staggers into shirts and underwear, frantically shoving them aside. Suddenly he is in the open, camera panning to show Densel lifting himself over the back fence. Brown fires, Densel clutching at his shoulder before he drops from sight. Brown leaps forward and we hear the roar of an automobile engine in the alley. Climbing on some boxes, Brown lunges for the top of the fence, looks over.

EXTERIOR ALLEY—NIGHT
From Brown's angle. A heavy sedan careens down the alley, turning into next street.

EXTERIOR BROWNSTONE—NIGHT
At fence. Brown, disgusted, turns away, jumping to the ground. He runs off in the direction of the building.

INTERIOR BROWNSTONE FRONT—NIGHT
Lower hallway and vestibule favoring Mrs. Neil who stands with her back pressed against the wall, eyes averted, her face frozen

into lines of horror. Several doors are open now, spilling light into the scene and the tenants are talking in excited whispers. We see the man who first opened a door, and then notice the taxi driver who is looking down as Brown comes in through back door.

TENANT: ... They were shooting right past me! So I ducked quick and—

He breaks off as Brown goes past, the murmur of voices dying suddenly as the group watches Brown who pulls up short, staring down in hushed silence of the hall. Camera tilts down to reveal Forbes' body sprawled on the stairs, one arm extended still holding the gun. Slowly Brown kneels.

TAXI DRIVER: *(shattering the silence)* Your friend's dead, mister.

Brown's lips tighten. He touches Forbes' face as the camera moves closer. His eyes go to the cigar lying on the floor, then to the ashes spilled on Forbes' coat. Slowly, without seeming to think, he brushes them off.

MRS. NEIL: *(offstage)* You heard him! He's dead! Why don't you get me out of here?

Reverse in hall. Brown gets to his feet, still staring down at Forbes.

MRS. NEIL: *(hysterically)* Well, what're you waiting for?

BROWN: Shut up! *(turns to the tenant)* You saw this. Did you get a look at the guy in the hall?

TENANT: Not his face. I was trying to remember. He was about your height. Wore an overcoat ...

He wets his lips thinking.

BROWN: Go on. I'm an officer. *(shows his badge)* Sergeant Brown— Los Angeles. What else about him?

TENANT: There was something about the coat ...

Mrs. Neil grabs Brown's arm.

MRS. NEIL: Listen, that guy may be back! Are we going to hang around here all night?

BROWN: *(to taxi driver)* Get her bag. *(to tenant)* You'd better phone the police.

Closer group as the driver picks up the suitcase. Brown turns, lifts phonograph case and steers Mrs. Neil for door.

TENANT: *(coming after them)* I know what it was—the coat had fur on it—dark fur on the collar.

10

BROWN: Okay, get on the phone—tell 'em what you know and tell 'em I'll wire a complete report.

He exits with Mrs. Neil through door, the driver following as the tenant steps to a wall telephone.

EXTERIOR BROWNSTONE FRONT—NIGHT
Medium shot—Brown, Mrs. Neil and driver hurrying down steps to taxi. Brown glancing at his watch as he helps Mrs. Neil into the cab.

BROWN: *(slamming door)* Right back where we came from—only faster!

The driver climbs in front seat and, as the taxi wheels away we—

DISSOLVE

INTERIOR MOVING TAXI—NIGHT—(PROCESS)
Brown clubs his thigh savagely with his fist in a fit of self-reproach.

BROWN: *(to himself)* The one time I let him go first, it happens.

MRS. NEIL: Forbes?

BROWN: He was getting old and slow. Put a live bomb in his hand, you could count ten. I'll never forgive myself.

MRS. NEIL: Oh, this is fine. Some protection they send me. An old man who walks right into it and a weeper.

BROWN: How do you expect me to feel? We were partners six years. He broke me in. He and his wife—*(remembers)* Julie—what am I going to tell her? *(shakes his head wearily; takes out notebook and pencil)*

EXTERIOR CHICAGO LOOP—NIGHT—(STOCK)
Long shot—the taxi in traffic.

INTERIOR MOVING TAXI—NIGHT—(PROCESS)
Mrs. Neil has relaxed a little but she is still tense. Brown is making notes in his book.

MRS. NEIL: What're you doing—keeping score?

BROWN: Yeah—one down, two to go.

MRS. NEIL: Don't kid about it. Whoever that was, they were trying to get me! How long do you think my luck will hold?

Brown puts the book away.

BROWN: As long as there're cops like Forbes around to get killed for you.

She gives him a slightly contemptuous smile. The fear is leaving her and she seems to be studying Brown as though he might offer advantages beyond protection.

MRS. NEIL: Like you, I suppose.

BROWN: Yeah, like me.

MRS. NEIL: My taste doesn't usually run to cops, but you might not be such dull company at that.

BROWN: *(turning to her)* Mrs. Neil, you and I better get something straight—you're just a job to me, a C.O.D. package for the L.A. Grand Jury, and there's no joy in it. I don't like you any more than Forbes did, but he got himself murdered for you—and maybe I will, too. That's what they pay me for. Do we understand each other?

Mrs. Neil is tapping a cigarette on her fingernail, a disbelieving smile on her face.

MRS. NEIL: Relax, Percy, your shield's untarnished. I've changed my mind.

He thrusts a cigarette in his mouth and lights it.

MRS. NEIL: *(continued)* I wouldn't want any of that nobility to rub off on me.

BROWN: *(flicks match away)* It won't—if you keep your distance.

Closer shot—favoring Mrs. Neil. She smiles, gently taking his lighted cigarette and pressing it to her own.

MRS. NEIL: *(blows smoke in his face)* All the way to the coast?

Pained, Brown retrieves his cigarette.

BROWN: *(thinking aloud)* Poor Forbes.

MRS. NEIL: *(unfeelingly)* What about poor Forbes?

Brown looks at her witheringly.

BROWN: He owed me five bucks.

New angle. Leaning forward Brown raps on the driver's panel.

BROWN: Driver—about two blocks from the station let me out.

He shuts the panel, and begins fumbling some bills from his wallet, Mrs. Neil showing sudden concern.

12

MRS. NEIL: What's the idea?

Brown removes an envelope from his pocket and stuffs the money inside.

BROWN: You're on your own till the train starts.

BROWN: *(continued) (hands her envelope)* Tickets and money. Pay the driver.

MRS. NEIL: *(puzzled)* I don't get it.

BROWN: *(glancing at watch)* Just do as I tell you. So far nobody's spotted you, and nobody knows what you look like; but they've seen me—and if they start shooting in my direction I don't want you hit.

MRS. NEIL: *(suspiciously)* You're sure it isn't the other way around?

BROWN: When you get to the station, walk, don't run, to the platform. Carry your own bag. Go straight to car ten, compartment B and lock yourself in. If the lights are on, turn 'em off and leave 'em off— and don't forget to pull the shade.

The cab stops and Brown reaches for the door handle, his eyes on Mrs. Neil.

MRS. NEIL: Suppose I stand you up? I'm not too keen on this grand jury business.

BROWN: *(ominously)* You've forgotten the guy with the fur collar, Mrs. Neil. You can't stand *him* up. By tomorrow morning they'd be fishing you out of the Chicago River. *(opens door, turns)* See you aboard.

Mrs. Neil stares at him in tight-lipped silence. Brown grins and climbs out, carrying the phonograph.

EXTERIOR CHICAGO STREET—NIGHT

At taxi. Brown slams the door and waves the driver on. As the taxi moves off, Brown shoots a glance behind him, tightens his coat against the biting wind, then walks briskly across the wet street, dodging traffic.

DISSOLVE

EXTERIOR CHICAGO RAILROAD STATION—NIGHT

Full shot—at taxi stand. The taxi grinds to a stop, the driver assisting Mrs. Neil to the curb. She pays him and, ignoring a Red

13

Cap, starts into the station, carrying her suitcase. She enters through swinging doors, the wind tugging at her coat. Camera pans to another set of doors beyond which we see a cigar and newsstand inside. A sallow-looking guy is standing at the counter, cleaning his nails. This is Joe Kemp. He wears glasses and his back is to us—and also to the other doors and waiting room which Mrs. Neil entered. A foot or two further down the counter stands a slightly old man, flipping through a magazine. He is dressed in better taste than Kemp and radiates greater authority and poise. His name is Vinnie Yost. The eyes of both are on the proprietor of the stand who is telephoning.

INTERIOR NEWSSTAND—NIGHT
Shooting past Kemp towards proprietor on telephone and taking in Yost.
PROPRIETOR: *(into phone—checks watch)* . . . leaves in five minutes. I'll tell them.
The proprietor hangs up and steps over to Kemp and Yost, resting his elbows on the counter. They look at him questioningly. Yost comes closer.
PROPRIETOR: *(continued) (to Yost)* Densel had bad luck. He got winged, too.
YOST: Up to us, huh?
PROPRIETOR: Tail Brown. She's with him.
KEMP: What's she look like?
PROPRIETOR: He never saw her face. Just keep your eye on the cop. They'll be on the train together someplace. Better get started.
YOST: Who covers us—in case?
PROPRIETOR: Leave that to Densel.
YOST: *(to Kemp)* I'll be in the club car.
Kemp nods, exiting off. Yost replaces magazine, then follows.

DISSOLVE

INTERIOR CHICAGO RAILROAD STATION—NIGHT
At Ticket Gate. Camera begins moving with Brown as he approaches a line of passengers waiting to have their tickets checked

at the gate leading to platform. Over shot we hear the announcer's voice booming on the p.a. system.

ANNOUNCER: . . . Central Pacific train number five. The Golden West Limited, departing track eight for Kansas City, Albuquerque, Los Angeles . . .

Camera pans to pillar as Kemp, spotting Brown, reacts and saunters after him in the line.

Closer at Ticket Gate. Brown has his ticket envelope out and is standing with several other passengers moving past the conductor. Kemp edges into scene behind him. Brown turns at this moment, noticing Kemp. Brown hands his tickets to the conductor, he sneaks another look at Kemp, catching him staring. Kemp quickly busies himself with his own tickets and holds his place in the line as Brown passes through the gate onto the platform, the camera trucking ahead of him. He stuffs the envelope in his pocket, walking briskly, but it is apparent Kemp is on his mind when he stops a moment to light a cigarette, managing another look behind as he throws the match away. He walks on.

INTERIOR CHICAGO RAILROAD PLATFORM—NIGHT
Kemp is coming through the gate, camera panning as he moves along with other hurrying passengers. To our right we see the shining rear coaches of the Gold Coast Limited, vestibule doors open, porters on hand to assist passengers into train—and farther on Brown who is just stopping at a magazine cart, where he purchases a magazine, purposely stalling until Kemp is forced to pass behind him. Brown, without seeming to notice, throws down a coin. Then, instead of continuing in his former direction, he abruptly walks back, opening the magazine to flip through the pages, camera panning him through a group of passengers, red caps and baggage trucks.

Close trucking shot on Kemp. Out of the corner of his eye he has observed Brown's tactics and is forced to lag his steps, finally stopping for a good look behind.

Reverse angle past Kemp. Brown, apparently engrossed in the magazine, is standing opposite one of the rear cars. Camera

15

begins moving with Kemp as he strolls off towards the magazine cart and goes through the motions of buying a magazine.

Closeup—Brown. He sneaks a look towards Kemp, quickly folding the magazine as he turns away.

Closeup—Kemp. His back, for a moment, is to Brown. He is paying for the magazine.

Travelling shot on baggage truck as it moves towards Brown, who steps behind it, keeping the rolling truck between him and Kemp. The latter, when he turns, reacts to the fact that Brown has momentarily disappeared. He hurries towards the spot where Brown was standing, and stops, looking both ways on platform.

Dolly shot behind baggage truck, as Brown keeps pace with it, then ducks into the open vestibule of a car.

Reverse angle past Kemp. He sees the baggage truck, but no sign of Brown. It occurs to him what may have happened, however, and he runs along the length of the train.

Another angle at compartment car. Kemp hurries past the open vestibule, then doubles back, camera moving to show Brown passing from one car to the next. Satisfied, Kemp continues along train in the direction Brown is travelling inside.

INTERIOR COMPARTMENT CAR—NIGHT

Corridor alongside rooms (not visible from platform). Brown approaches numbers "A" and "B" at the vestibule end of the corridor—just as the Red Cap emerges from "A".

RED CAP: Your case is inside, sir.

BROWN: Thanks.

Brown peels him off a bill, entering the compartment and closing the door.

INTERIOR PLATFORM

Shooting towards Brown's compartment. Kemp slows down and we are able to see Brown enter the compartment, step over to the window and draw the shade. The adjoining window is dark. Kemp moves along the train a short distance, stops, looking back. All doubts removed, he pulls an envelope from his pocket and

16

strides over to the conductor and porter who are standing at the open door to Brown's car.

INTERIOR BROWN'S COMPARTMENT—NIGHT
Brown, who has been peering through a crack in the shade, steps back and knocks on the connecting door to the next compartment.
BROWN: *(softly)* It's me, Brown—open up.
There is a pause, then the catch clicks, the door opening. Mrs. Neil stands there in the dark, still in her street clothes.
MRS. NEIL: Well—are we okay?
BROWN: *(entering)* Tell you in a minute.
He shuts the door.

INTERIOR MRS. NEIL'S COMPARTMENT—NIGHT
It is in darkness. Brown, crossing to window, flattens his face against the drawn shade, peering through the crack in the side in an effort to spot Kemp.
Over Brown's shoulder. The platform and side of car through crack in shade as we see Kemp get aboard the car, the conductor glancing at watch, then turning to give the starting signals.
BROWN: The answer's no.
Camera pulls back as Brown turns on the small lamp over the bed and the subdued glow reveals Mrs. Neil leaning against the bulkhead, tense and worried. Her suitcase is open on the berth.
MRS. NEIL: They know I'm here, don't they?
BROWN: Take it easy.
MRS. NEIL: Who followed you—the guy with the fur collar?
BROWN: No, from the same stable, I guess—some creep with a one-track mind—
Closeup—Mrs. Neil
MRS. NEIL: *(irritatingly)* What're you gonna do? How you gonna handle it? Why'd you let him follow you? What're you gonna do? They promised me protection! They said it would—
Closeup—Brown.

17

BROWN: Shut up! Shut up, you hear! I got enough on my mind! It's a rotten *detail*! I didn't like it from the start! My partner's dead and it's my fault! *He's* dead and *you're* alive! *(bitterly)* Some exchange!
He breaks off as we hear the buzzer sounding in the next compartment. Brown, motioning Mrs. Neil to silence, quickly opens the connecting door, starts out.
BROWN: *(continued) (turns, whispers)* Lock it!
He exits, closing door, which Mrs. Neil hurriedly locks.

INTERIOR BROWN'S COMPARTMENT—NIGHT
Brown crosses to outside door, opens it. The conductor is standing in the corridor with Joe Kemp.
CONDUCTOR: This gentleman's lost a brief case. *(peers in)* We thought the red cap might've put it in here by mistake.
Kemp edges into compartment.
BROWN: I don't think so . . . *(indicates two suitcases)* These are mine.
KEMP: *(edging in)* It was a pig-skin case.
CONDUCTOR: *(to Kemp)* Well, we'll keep looking. *(to Brown)* Sorry to have bothered you.
He starts out, but Kemp is staring boldly at the connecting door.
KEMP: *(watching door)* I'm sure it's in this car . . .

INTERIOR MRS. NEIL'S COMPARTMENT—NIGHT
She has her face pressed against the door, listening, and Kemp's voice comes over shot from adjoining compartment.
KEMP'S VOICE: What about that next room?
Mrs. Neils draws a deep breath and holds it.
BROWN'S VOICE: That room's empty . . .

INTERIOR BROWN'S COMPARTMENT—NIGHT
Brown, Kemp and conductor as Brown continues.
BROWN: *(hurriedly—to conductor)* . . . As a matter of fact, conductor, I wanted to speak to you about it.
Closeup—Kemp, a look of disbelief on his face.
BROWN'S VOICE: My partner was held over in Chicago and won't be using the space.
New angle

18

BROWN: *(shows conductor tickets)* Both rooms are paid for to the coast and I'd like a rebate ...

CONDUCTOR: *(making note on pad)* I'll wire the passenger agent in Kansas City. We'll try to sell it there.

The conductor starts out, Kemp lingering behind.

BROWN: Much obliged. *(to Kemp)* Hope you find your case.

KEMP: I will.

Reverse in compartment as Kemp exits after conductor, Brown shutting door. Over shot we hear cries of "All aboard—board!" There is a slight jolt forward as the train starts. Brown hesitates a moment, then steps to connecting door, rapping twice.

BROWN: It's all right.

Mrs. Neil opens door, looks out.

MRS. NEIL: *(frightened)* That was the one, wasn't it?

BROWN: Yeah—He seems to have *me* spotted, anyhow.

Brown shakes a cigarette out of pack, mouths it, thinking.

MRS. NEIL: Then I haven't got a chance! He'll be back! And when he finds me, goodbye!

Her hand trembles as she pushes her hair in place.

BROWN: *(lighting up)* Maybe not.

MRS. NEIL: Are you kidding? I can't hang out the window and the upper berth's too small!

Brown crowds past her into compartment.

INTERIOR MRS. NEIL'S COMPARTMENT—NIGHT

Camera trucks forward as Brown enters, looks around. His attention seems to be on the upper berth which is locked shut against the ceiling.

MRS. NEIL: *(watching him, nervously)* What're you going to do— measure it?

BROWN: *(turns)* You gave me an idea.

MRS. NEIL: *(ready to crack)* Well, I don't like it already. I'm in a spot, Brown—and your job is to protect me—it's your move!

Brown slips his revolver out of holster, checks the chamber.

BROWN: *(deadly serious)* You're wrong—it's *his*. *(replaces gun)* And we're going to let him make it, Mrs. Neil.

On Mrs. Neil's alarmed reaction, we:

DISSOLVE

EXTERIOR RAILROAD YARDS—NIGHT
The streamliner glides towards us, picking up speed. There is a steady, pounding roar from the diesel locomotive as it whisks past, then a fast checkerboarding of lighted windows.

DISSOLVE

INTERIOR CLUB-LOUNGE CAR—NIGHT
Brown enters through glass door and we note the gleaming, modern car, which is midway in the train, with an inviting bar at the far end facing the tastefully appointed interior. A waiter moves among the passengers serving them drinks, as others read papers or listen to the piped-in music. A soft hum of conversation blends with the muffled song of the rails. Brown continues towards the bar. Kemp appears at the opposite end, passing Brown in the aisle. Lights flash by outside the windows as the streamliner settles down to its ninety-mile-an-hour speed.
The camera follows Brown to a table next to the bar, where he sits down next to a very attractive, smartly-dressed young woman whom we shall know as Ann Sinclair.
Closer at table—Brown and Ann. Brown's back is to Kemp, but he can observe him in a small mirror on the partition, camera tilting up to show Kemp just sitting down in a leather chair, his eyes on Brown. Ann glances at Brown over her drink. His attention is on the mirror. The waiter steps over from bar.

WAITER: Yessir?

BROWN: *(preoccupied—indicates Ann's drink)* Same as hers.
Camera pulls back as Ann gives him a cold disapproving stare as the waiter steps to bar. She has misinterpreted Brown's intentions and, as he looks at her, she quickly rises, holding her drink.

ANN: *(to waiter—at bar)* I'll finish this at the other table.
She turns and the train lurches, throwing her against Brown. The drink splashes over his coat and trousers.

ANN: *(continued) (apologetically)* Oh, I'm terribly sorry . . . !
Brown half rises, brushing at his coat.

BROWN: Don't I get a chaser?
The waiter returns with Brown's drink and steps to bar again.
ANN: *(to Brown)* I'm really sorry—at least let me pay for your drink.
BROWN: No—*this* one's on me, too. *(to waiter)* Would you fix her another.
ANN: *(smiles)* The same as his.
She sits down again. Brown lays down a five dollar bill.
BROWN: Someday they'll get around to paving this track—and then these accidents won't happen.
Closer—favoring Brown. He shoots a glance in the mirror, begins nervously stirring his drink as Ann watches him curiously. Seemingly, he has forgotten the girl and the drink. The waiter returns and serves Ann.
ANN: *(watching Brown)*Here's to better tracks—and steadier nerves.
She lifts her glass. Brown looks at her sharply.
BROWN: Mine or yours?
ANN: Yours. You'll get there just as fast if you relax.
BROWN: *(smiles)* That sounded sort of familiar—but you're right. I'm a little on edge tonight.
They drink. He fumbles a pack of cigarettes out, then looks in the mirror, reacting, as the camera tilts up and we notice that Kemp is gone.
Reverse angle at table as Brown spins around, camera panning to reveal Kemp's empty chair.
BROWN: *(jumping up)* Excuse me . . . !
He strides off, leaving drinks and money, as Ann reacts in surprise, watching him as he pushes through the glass door at end of car.

INTERIOR CLUB-LOUNGE CAR—NIGHT
Corridor. Brown approaching a long narrow passageway leading to vestibule, bracing himself against the swaying coach. The door to the lavatory swings back and an enormous fat man, Sam Jennings, squeezes into the corridor, effectively blocking it.
BROWN: *(behind him)* Pardon me . . .
Jennings starts to go, but his coat is caught in the door. Brown, waiting impatiently, frees the coat.

21

JENNINGS: Thank you, my friend.
He pulls out his handkerchief and wipes his face.
BROWN: I'd like to get through.
JENNINGS: *(waddles ahead)* Sorry, this train wasn't designed for my tonnage.
They finally reach a bulge in the corridor at the vestibule and Jennings leans against the bulkhead so Brown can slither past.
JENNINGS: *(continued) (sighs)* Nobody loves a fat man—except his grocer and tailor.
Brown exits through to next car.

INTERIOR BROWN'S COMPARTMENT—NIGHT
Close on door as it opens inward and we see the "A" on the panel. Then it shuts, camera pulling back as Kemp enters quickly, shutting the door, bolting it. He takes out his gun and stands a moment, holding it in readiness. Then he looks in the lavatory, then steps over the two suitcases and tries the knob on the connecting door. He turns it slowly and then flings the door open to Mrs. Neil's compartment. His face registers surprise; he enters.

INTERIOR MRS. NEIL'S COMPARTMENT—NIGHT
The room is empty of everything—bags, clothes and occupants. In fact it appears as though nobody had used it, or even so much as touched the neatly-made-up lower berth. Frowning, Kemp rips open the lavatory door, starts to leave, then hesitates, his gaze wandering to the upper berth, which is closed against the bulkhead. The camera tilts up as he extracts a porter's berth key from his pocket and inserts it in the lock, twisting the key. The berth falls open, revealing nothing but bedding.
Close on Kemp—his face a study in angry bewilderment. An idea is forming, however, and he darts into Brown's compartment. Corridor—at opposite end. Brown, a satisfied smile on his face, lights a cigarette, obviously aware of what is taking place, and steps into vestibule.

INTERIOR BROWN'S COMPARTMENT—NIGHT

22

As Kemp closes the upper berth here, his frustration increasing. His eyes search every corner of the room; then, resigned, he puts revolver away and opens the corridor door just as the conductor is passing. Before he can close it, the conductor has doubled back, and Kemp is trapped. ,

CONDUCTOR: You're Mr. Kemp, aren't you—Joseph Kemp?

KEMP: That's right.

The conductor hands him a telegram.

CONDUCTOR: Wire for you. By the way, this isn't your space, is it?

KEMP: *(uneasily—pockets wire)* No—I was looking for that brief-case—thought it might've got in the next room, only I was wrong.

CONDUCTOR: *(admonishing him)* I'm afraid you were, Mr. Kemp.

He stands back, waiting for Kemp to leave.

KEMP: *(starts out, forcing grin)* Well, you can't blame a guy for trying, can you?

He exits into corridor, the conductor shutting the door.

Vestibule past Brown down corridor as Kemp starts towards us along full length of corridor, pulling out the telegram and reading as he walks. The conductor exits at the rear and Brown backs away, camera panning as he enters vestibule of next car forward. The pullman section from Brown's angle. Jennings, the fat man, is approaching.

INTERIOR VESTIBULE
as Kemp comes through, opening door to Pullman.

INTERIOR CORRIDOR—PULLMAN
Brown, caught between two converging forces, opens the first door he can find, stepping into a compartment a moment before Kemp appears at one end of the corridor and Jennings at the other.

INTERIOR PULLMAN COMPARTMENT—NIGHT
It is in complete darkness, save for a changing pattern of lights and shadows against the window, a faint illumination that reveals Brown flattened against the door, listening. Suddenly, a figure sits up in the lower berth. This is Tommy Sinclair, aged seven.

TOMMY: *(quietly)* There's somebody in here.

Brown whirls as an elderly woman (Mrs. Troll) in the upper berth switches on the light, reacting in alarm at sight of Brown.

MRS. TROLL: *(blinking awake)* What do you want? Who are you?

Tommy slips out of the berth and gives Brown the once-over.

TOMMY: I know—he's a train robber!

BROWN: *(stalling for time)* No—just a passenger. I got in the wrong compartment.

MRS. TROLL: *(indignantly)* Indeed you did.

BROWN: *(reaches for door)* Mine must be in the car ahead.

TOMMY: *(craftily)* Do you carry a gun?

MRS. TROLL: Tommy! Let the man be. He made a mistake, so let him go about his business.

BROWN: *(gratefully)* Thank you, madame.

TOMMY: But if his business is robbing people, we oughta call the police or something.

BROWN: Good night, son.

He manages an exit, Tommy staring at the door, unconvinced.

TOMMY: *(suddenly)* Hey—the next car doesn't have compartments! It's a day coach ...! *(starts for door)* I'll betcha he's a robber ...!

He starts to open door.

MRS. TROLL: You come back here, Tommy! This instant! Close that door ...!

She makes a move to climb down from berth.

TOMMY: *(shuts door)* All right, but I'm going to lock it.

He slips the catch, standing in worried thought a moment before turning back to berth.

INTERIOR CLUB CAR LOUNGE—NIGHT

Kemp enters and finds a seat. Yost is sitting across the aisle, reading a newspaper. He cocks a questioning eyebrow at Kemp. Kemp shakes his head slightly and shrugs—no sign of her. Yost nods—okay, I'll handle it—and lights a cigar.

INTERIOR BROWN'S COMPARTMENT CAR—NIGHT

Corridor outside ladies' lounge as Brown enters to curtains, looks around, he knocks quickly on the bulkhead. Mrs. Neil peers out. She is in negligee now with the robe pulled around her.

BROWN: *(nervously)* All clear—give me the suitcase.

Mrs. Neil nods, hands out suitcase, then follows into corridor, carrying the phonograph case. They hurry down the corridor.

INTERIOR COMPARTMENT CAR—NIGHT
Down corridor as Mrs. Neil comes through, almost running, Brown behind her. He rips open the door to his compartment, shoving her in and follows.

INTERIOR BROWN'S COMPARTMENT—NIGHT
He bolts the door as Mrs. Neil goes through connecting door into next compartment, camera panning as Brown follows. We see Mrs. Neil drop the phonograph case and flop down on the berth. Brown slides her suitcase into the room.

MRS. NEIL: Well, did he go for it or didn't he?

BROWN: He bit—searched both rooms. *(grins)* You're the little girl that wasn't here.

MRS. NEIL: Lucky me.

BROWN: Yeah—chances are they won't look for you here again.

MRS. NEIL: What do you mean, *they?*

BROWN: Just a hunch—these birds travel in pairs sometimes. But don't worry about it. You're still a mystery to 'em. It's a long train and you're not the only woman passenger aboard.

MRS. NEIL: I'm the only one who won't *sleep* tonight.

Closeup—Brown.

BROWN: I know a woman who won't sleep for a lot of nights.

MRS. NEIL: *(offstage)* Who?

BROWN: Forbes' wife.

BROWN'S COMPARTMENT—NIGHT
He steps into his own compartment, shuts the connecting door and slips the catch. He takes off his coat, hangs it up, pulls his tie loose and opens his collar. He flips on the seat-light and turns off

25

the top light. He is about to return to the seat when the thought strikes him and he inspects the catch on the door leading to the corridor. He opens the door slightly, works the catch once or twice, then, satisfied, he is about to shut the door when he sees something in the corridor. His hand goes to his shoulder holster.

INTERIOR CORRIDOR—NIGHT
Over Brown's shoulder, we see Yost at the door. He nods pleasantly and takes the cigar from his mouth.
YOST: Mr. Brown, I have a business proposition that might interest you.
Brown steps back quickly, gun in hand, opens the door wider, yanks Yost in, the gun to his belly, shuts the door and locks it. He studies Yost for a moment. Yost remains impassive; he raises his hands. Brown frisks him swiftly and none too gently.
YOST: I never carry one. Matter of fact, I've never even held one in my hand. Got no stomach for it. Okay to put my hands down?
Brown shoves him back into one of the seats.
YOST: *(continued) (reprovingly)* You don't have to do that. *(pause)* My name is Yost, Vincent Yost.
BROWN: So?
YOST: I'd just like us to have a little talk, that's all. We're ready to make a deal.
YOST: *(continued)* You have her. We want her. How much? It's as simple as that.
BROWN: Consider yourself under arrest.
YOST: For doing what?
BROWN: Attempted bribery. *(reaches behind him toward call-button)*
YOST: Me? Attempted bribery? You'd never make it stick, Mr. Brown. I'm Vincent Yost, sales executive for the Mid-West Equipment Company, Chicago. I've never even gotten so much as a parking ticket.
Brown lowers his hand. Yost settles himself more comfortably.

INTERIOR COMPARTMENT—NIGHT
Yost shifts his legs.
YOST: Mr. Brown, we want to settle this matter reasonably.

26

BROWN: That why you killed Forbes?

YOST: Forbes? Oh. I didn't know. I'm sorry. We got word of your coming so late. We had to improvise. Believe me, my firm doesn't like to do business that way.

BROWN: His wife will be glad to learn it. Also his two daughters. And the bank that holds the mortgage on his house.

YOST: Believe me, we like to avoid such things. It's to our own interest. That's why I'm here. I know there can be a meeting of the minds if you'll listen to me.

BROWN: Not interested.

YOST: Not interested in, oh, twenty-five thousand dollars? Thirty? You name the figure, Mr. Brown. I'm sure we can strike a favorable bargain. My firm has a large investment in this matter and several of our key personnel are involved.

BROWN: Not at any price.

YOST: You dismiss it so lightly, I can see you've never really known what it feels like to have a large sum of money all your own. May I put my hand in my pocket?

Yost takes Brown's silence for consent and brings forth a bulky wallet from which he extracts a sheaf of bills. He places the money on Brown's lap.

YOST: *(continued)* Five thousand dollars. A sample. Imagine what it must be like to have six, seven, ten times as much, all your own. How much is it a policeman earns? Three hundred a month? Four hundred? And you have to buy your own bullets, isn't it so? We offer you a fortune. And what do we ask in return?

BROWN: What?

YOST: That you point her out, then look the other way. Really, very little. And at no risk to your good name. You can go through all the motions of guarding her until—the accident occurs.

BROWN: No.

Yost: Now, why do you say that? What is there about the contract you don't like?

BROWN: I don't like murder.

YOST: Of a woman like Mrs. Neil? A gangster's wife. A low type. Believe me, the world is better off without her. What can she possibly mean to you?

27

Brown picks up the money, studies it a moment, then tosses it back to Yost.

YOST: *(continued)* Just think it over. Think of what you can do with a lot of money. Live better. Travel, perhaps. If you're really concerned about Forbes' family, you can give it to them. *(sees he has interested Brown for the first time)* Yes. You can *soften* their loss. *(gets to his feet)* Meanwhile, of course, we'll keep looking. We'll get her whether you give her to us or not, you know, so don't take too long. A shame if you missed your opportunity. I'm sure you'll find me when you make up your mind!

He nods pleasantly to Brown, goes to the door, slips the catch and exits, closing the door behind him. Brown nibbles at his knuckles, deep in thought.

DISSOLVE

Fast traveling camera with the streamliner—day
The whistle sounds a deep note as the diesel locomotive whips into a curve, the morning sun glinting on bright metal cars.

INTERIOR COMPARTMENT CAR—DAY

Brown's compartment. The shade is up and the west Kansas landscape is flying past outside the window as Brown emerges from lavatory, slipping into his coat, tucking his revolver firmly into the holster. He turns as the latch rattles on the connecting door. Mrs. Neil opens it, still in her robe.

MRS. NEIL: *(indicating gun)* What're you going to do—shoot something for breakfast?

BROWN: Sure—name it.

MRS. NEIL: Eggs, bacon, toast, a bucket of coffee and some cigarettes. I'm famished, Brown.

BROWN: Okay, I'll share it with you. I don't want them counting trays. *(tosses her a pack of cigarettes)* Here's some smokes. Get your appetite under control while I find a waiter.

MRS. NEIL: This is a modern train. Why don't you ring for him?

BROWN: Because I want to look around first. So stay in there and keep your door locked.

Mrs. Neil: *(closing door)* I like my bacon crisp—with lots of butter on the toast, please.
Brown waits until her lock catches, then exits into corridor.

INTERIOR PULLMAN—DAY
Sections—some of the berths still made up, others being converted into seats by the porter. We see Kemp backing into aisle, his head emerging from the curtains. He has a shaving kit in his hand, his back to Brown who appears at end of car, and stops, watching Kemp who moves towards men's lavatory, disappearing.
Closer—at Kemp's section. Brown enters quickly and, while the porter is looking the other way, pulls the curtains aside, entering the section.

INTERIOR KEMP'S SECTION
It has been partially made up, the bedding is gone and the two seats are back in place. Brown dives into Kemp's suitcase, fumbling through the contents.

INTERIOR MEN'S LAVATORY
Kemp is bent over one of the wash bowls, scrubbing his teeth. Two men are shaving at the other bowls and a third enters to wait his turn. Kemp straightens, shaking water from his toothbrush, and wipes his face with a towel. Then he runs an exploring hand across his beard, resolves it's not worth shaving.
Kemp: *(to third man)* It's all yours.
Passenger: *(taking his place)* Thanks. Pretty heavy traffic this morning.
Kemp nods, steps away, selects another mirror and runs a comb through his hair.

INTERIOR KEMP'S SECTION
Brown finishes with the suitcase, obviously discouraged, and glances around. His eyes light on Kemp's coat, swinging from a hook, and he hurriedly goes through the pockets, discovering the telegram, which he yanks from the envelope and reads:

29

INSERT TELEGRAM:

JOSEPH KEMP GOLDEN WEST LIMITED ENROUTE L.A. DELIVER VIA GALESBURG: ATTRACTION DEFINITELY ON BOARD YOUR TRAIN. EXPECT ACTION BEFORE ALBUQUERQUE. DENSEL WILL CONTACT.

Back to scene. Brown replaces the telegram in envelope and stuffs it back in Kemp's coat; then he turns, pulling back curtains.

Pullman aisle as Brown emerges from Kemp's section at the exact moment Tommy Sinclair, wearing robe and slippers, runs into scene and catches him in the act. Brown, trapped, turns his back on the boy, but he has taken only two steps when Tommy starts after him. Camera dollies with them.

TOMMY: Hey—wait a minute! I know you. *(darts in front of Brown)* I saw you sneak out of there! You said you had a compartment!

Brown is forced to stop as the porter pokes his head out of a section and several passengers draw the curtains back from their berths.

BROWN: *(holds out his hand)* Take it easy, son—let's talk this over.

Tommy leaps back and we see Kemp enter scene from corridor.

TOMMY: Get your hands off me! *(to passengers)* He's a robber. Last night he snuck in on us an' I just saw him sneaking out of—

He breaks off as Brown suddenly picks him up.

BROWN: *(hastily)* That's a good boy—up we go! *(starts off)* Hang on now. We'll find mother.

Tommy hauls off and lands a blow on Brown's chin. Camera trucking forward.

TOMMY: *(struggling)* Put me down! Put me down!

Brown ducks another blow.

PORTER: Say, he's some little scrapper . . . !

BROWN: We're training him that way.

He disappears with Tommy into corridor. Camera holds on Kemp, staring after them curiously.

Pullman corridor outside compartments—Brown entering with Tommy to meet Mrs. Troll midway in the passage.

BROWN: Here's your boy, madame.

MRS. TROLL: Tommy, where on earth have you been?

BROWN: He got lost . . .

30

He loads Tommy into the woman's arms.

TOMMY: I did not! *(points at Brown)* He's got a gun under his arm. I felt it! Call the police!

MRS. TROLL: He's very excitable.

BROWN: *(backing off)* Probably feeding him wrong. Too many oats.

Mrs. Troll reaches for her compartment door.

TOMMY: *(protesting)* The police'll lock him up! *(Mrs. Troll opens her door)* They'll take his gun away!

The door closes. Brown, badly shaken, whips out a handkerchief, mops his forehead, camera pulling back as he crosses to water cooler near vestibule. He pours himself a drink in a paper cup, draws a deep breath, then turns as Kemp enters corridor at the other end. The two men exchange blank looks, then Kemp squeezes past.

BROWN: *(casually)* You find your case yet?

Kemp turns, surprised.

KEMP: *(with deep meaning)* No, but I'm still looking.

He exits into vestibule as Brown crumples the paper cup and makes a move to follow. Ann's voice over shot stops him.

ANN'S VOICE: Good morning ...

Reverse as Brown whirls, camera panning to show the girl just coming out of the second compartment.

BROWN: Oh, hello—how are you? *(anxious to be off)* I was just on my way to the dining car.

He grabs some telegraph blanks out of holder.

ANN: So am I.

He steps to vestibule door, camera moving forward to reveal Kemp just passing into next car.

ANN: *(continued)* Still rushing, I see.

He holds the vestibule door open for her, peering ahead, holding telegraph blanks.

BROWN: *(trying to keep Kemp in view)* Yeah, kind of busy this morning.

They exit into vestibule.

INTERIOR DINING CAR—DAY

Along corridor as Kemp approaches the entrance to the cafe proper, looking back just as Brown and Ann come in behind him.
ANN: *(to Brown)* You know, running around as much as you do must work up quite an appetite . . .
Kemp disappears into the cafe, camera panning as the head-waiter leads him down aisle of tables.
BROWN: *(watching—to Ann)* What'd you say?
At a rear table Kemp sits down opposite Jennings, the fat man.
ANN: I said you must be hungry.
BROWN: Oh, I can always eat . . .
The headwaiter comes over as a table for four is vacated, the two passengers leaving.
HEADWAITER: *(to Ann)* You people together?
BROWN: *(snaps out of it)* No, as a matter of fact I'm not eating. *(hastily to Ann)* Don't mind me—I've got something else on my mind.
ANN: *(opening purse—miffed)* Not food, obviously. *(hands him some bills)* Your change—remember? You went off and forgot it last night.
She abruptly leaves him, the head waiter leading her to the empty table, Brown staring after her, holding the money. It occurs to him that he has offended her and he follows.
Closer—at table as Brown sits down opposite Ann, who is next to the window, her back to the rear of the car. She picks up the menu.
BROWN: I guess I forgot something else, too, didn't I?
ANN: *(studying menu)* No, I took the tip out—your reputation's first-rate in the bar.
BROWN: Meaning it's not so good here. Anyhow, consider yourself apologized to. And I'm really not hungry.
He begins scribbling on one of the telegraph blanks.
BROWN: *(continued) (preoccupied)* Excuse me—Just a wire to the home office. *(frowns)* How do you spell "immediate"?
ANN: Two M's. And I wish you'd get those nerves quieted down.
BROWN: I'm working on it . . .
She fills in her order on pad as Brown continues writing. The waiter appears.
ANN: *(to waiter)* Toast and coffee. The gentleman's not having any.

WAITER: *(exiting)* Yes, mam.
Brown sneaks a glance at Kemp and Jennings.
Kemp and Jennings at rear table—from Brown's angle. They are both staring at him, apparently discussing him, but turn away when he catches them at it. Jennings throws down some change and gets ponderously to his feet, creating some alarm among passengers sitting across the aisle as his bulk weaves with the motion of the train. He starts towards Brown as Kemp sips his coffee, managing to observe the fat man's progress.
Reverse at table. Jennings, stopping to allow a waiter to squeeze past, turns abruptly to Brown.
JENNINGS: Always meeting each other in tight places, aren't we?
BROWN: This makes twice.
He quickly folds the telegraph blank and stuffs it in his pocket as Jennings rests his hand on the empty chair next to Ann.
JENNINGS: As a matter of fact I wanted to speak to you—if you'll forgive the intrusion. My name's Jennings—Sam Jennings.
He bows to Ann, smiling. Brown is watching him narrowly.
BROWN: What's on your mind?
JENNINGS: *(jovially)* A little deal—possibly an accommodation for both of us, certainly for *me*. The gentleman at the other table informs me you are trying to dispose of an extra compartment. I'd like to take it off your hands.
Brown lights a cigarette and shakes his head.
BROWN: That's very kind of you, but I've decided to keep the compartment.
Jennings' face clouds.
JENNINGS: May I ask why? You can't sleep in two rooms at once.
BROWN: I'm afraid that's my business.
JENNINGS: *(angrily)* But this is preposterous! Yours is the only available space on the train and I'm in an upper berth! *(appealingly—to Ann)* Young lady, does that seem fair or equitable—me at three hundred pounds in a hat box while this fellow monopolizes two spacious suites?
ANN: *(hiding a smile)* Maybe he has his reasons.
BROWN: Sorry—that's the way it's got to be.
Jennings gives him a slow appraisal.

JENNINGS: *(coldly)* Possibly not. *(wheels his bulk)* We'll see what the conductor has to say about this . . .

Camera pulls back as he lumbers off, causing waiters to lean backwards across tables, balancing trays precariously over people's heads as the fat man exits into corridor. Brown rises, turns to Ann.

BROWN: *(crushes out cigarette)* I guess I'll have to do some explaining.

ANN: *(seriously)* Explain it to me sometime, too, will you?

Brown grins, exits off, camera panning back to reveal Kemp watching Ann.

At entrance to corridor as Brown starts through, doubles back and motions the head waiter, who steps closer, camera angling in Jennings who is disappearing along corridor.

BROWN: *(to head waiter)* I'm in car ten—room A. Send me some breakfast. Bacon, eggs, toast . . . *(watching Jennings)* Let's see . . .

HEAD WAITER: *(writing order)* Coffee, sir?

BROWN: That's it. Plenty of coffee.

He presses a bill into the head waiter's hand and starts down corridor just as Tommy Sinclair enters from vestibule, dragging Mrs. Troll who has him by the hand.

TOMMY: *(excitedly)* There he is! If you don't believe me, search him! The gun's right under his arm!

BROWN: *(placating)* Look, if you'll be a good boy, I'll show you that gun sometime.

He starts past, but Tommy spreads his hands across corridor.

TOMMY: Show it to me now!

MRS. TROLL: *(alarmed—to Brown)* Then you *have* got a gun . . .

Brown grabs Tommy under the arms and swings him out of the way.

BROWN: *All* robbers have guns, madame.

He bolts away.

MRS. TROLL: Why, I don't believe it!

TOMMY: Sure, I told you, didn't I? He never fooled *me.*

Mrs. Troll takes Tommy by the hand and they enter the cafe, camera pulling back as Tommy breaks away and runs ahead to the table where Ann is sitting.

Closer at table. Ann smiles as Tommy scrambles into a chair and the head waiter seats Mrs. Troll.

ANN: Well, how's my little boy this morning?

TOMMY: Swell, we caught a robber, but he got away. Nanny wouldn't believe me, would you, Nanny? Go on, tell her.

Camera pans as Kemp, seated at the rear of car, frowns in surprise, and slowly gets up, counting out a tip.

New angle at table—Tommy, Ann and Mrs. Troll.

MRS. TROLL: It was a little mix-up, Mrs. Sinclair. This man got in our room by mistake.

ANN: *(surprised)* Who was he?

MRS. TROLL: Just a passenger. I'm sure it was an accident.

TOMMY: It was not! He's sneaking all over the train . . . !

ANN: *(thoughtfully)* Well, that *is* odd . . . *(to Tommy)* I'd like to hear more about this, Tommy—but not now. What would you like for breakfast?

At this moment Kemp ambles past, turning to get a good look at Ann.

MRS. TROLL: *(sharply—to Tommy)* Tommy, you heard your mother. What do you want to eat?

TOMMY: I'm not hungry.

ANN: All right, we'll just have to order for you. *(signals waiter)* Waiter . . .

As the waiter comes over, camera follows Kemp to front of car, where he turns again, looks back at Ann.

Reverse past Kemp as Ann, aware that he paid her unusual notice, turns and their eyes meet. He steps into the corridor, camera moving with him as he pauses, his hand stealing for a moment under his coat—then he straightens, a satisfied smile on his face, and exits off.

INTERIOR VESTIBULE COMPARTMENT CAR—DAY

As Brown comes through, camera panning to include Jennings and the conductor who addresses Brown.

CONDUCTOR: Mr. Brown, I'd like a word with you.

BROWN: Okay, but I might as well tell you I don't want to sell that compartment.

35

JENNINGS: *(to conductor)* Isn't there some rule about this, conductor?

CONDUCTOR: Not that I know of, Mr. Jennings. If a passenger pays for space and doesn't use it, that's his business.

BROWN: The point is I may have use for that space. Or rather my partner will.

CONDUCTOR: I thought your partner stayed in Chicago.

BROWN: He took the plane. In fact he's joining me along the way— then we're going on to L. A. together.

JENNINGS: *(sighs)* All right, let's drop it.

CONDUCTOR: *(to Jennings)* I'll see what I can do for you at La Junta.
He exits back. Brown starts past Jennings, turns.

BROWN: Conductor—*(realizes he's out of earshot)* I meant to ask him how long we stop there.
Jennings is still a little surly.

JENNINGS: La Junta's a twelve-minute stop. *(taking out a big turnip of a watch)* Oughta be pulling in there in two minutes . . .

BROWN: Thanks . . .
Brown goes through door into his car, Jennings looking after him. Slowly he puts the watch away, purses his lips. There is a hard look on his face as he turns away—and a purposeful manner about him we have not noticed before.

INTERIOR BROWN'S COMPARTMENT—DAY
Brown enters, closing door. He pulls the telegraph blank from his pocket, sits down and begins writing. Slowly, the door to the connecting compartment opens and Mrs. Neil peers out through the slit.

MRS. NEIL: I'd have sworn I heard dishes rattle and smelled coffee.

BROWN: Don't worry, it's on the way. Any minute.

MRS. NEIL: I may not last that long. *(looks out window)* Say, the train's stopping. Where are we?

BROWN: La Junta, Colorado—and don't be peeking at the sights. Play cards or something.

MRS. NEIL: I can't—I ate the deck.
She closes the door.

36

EXTERIOR RAILROAD STATION LA JUNTA—DAY

The streamliner is rolling in amid the usual bustle of baggage trucks being wheeled into position, a group of onlookers walking from the station and small boys running to keep pace with the throbbing diesel. The twelve-car train comes to a gentle stop, porters opening doors as the check-up crew goes to work, examining journal boxes.

EXTERIOR TRAIN—DAY

Medium at section coach. Kemp gets off with several passengers who begin stretching their legs, walking slowly up the platform. Camera holds on Kemp as he follows, keeping close to the train, and heading in the direction of Brown's compartment car.

INTERIOR COMPARTMENT CAR—DAY

Corridor outside rooms "A" and "B." A waiter enters, bearing a tray heavy with breakfast dishes under metal covers. He presses the buzzer and, in a moment, Brown opens the door.

WAITER: Your breakfast, sir. *(looks past Brown)* You have a table ready?

Brown hurriedly takes the tray from him.

BROWN: I'll set it up myself.

WAITER: *(takes tray back)* I'll be happy to do it for you.

BROWN: *(seizes tray again)* Don't bother ... I'll handle it ...

At same moment, Ann enters corridor behind the waiter. She pulls up short at sight of Brown with the tray. Brown quickly hands the tray back to the startled waiter.

BROWN: *(continued)* What're you giving me this for?

WAITER: *(surprised)* It's your breakfast, sir. You said—

BROWN: Nothing of the kind! I don't eat breakfast!

ANN: *(taking it all in—smiles)* You know, for a man that's not hungry, you certainly go about getting food in strange ways.

BROWN: Me? I didn't order this. *(to waiter)* There's some mistake, waiter.

The waiter, baffled and juggling tray, takes a peek at the bill again.

37

WAITER: Begging your pardon, sir—it says room A, car ten ...

INTERIOR MRS. NEIL'S COMPARTMENT
She has the connecting door open a crack, the waiter's voice carrying over shot.
WAITER'S VOICE: ... Bacon, eggs, toast and extra coffee. Somebody ordered it.
BROWN'S VOICE: Not here, they didn't.
Mrs. Neil leans weakly against the door, a look of hopeless wrath on her face.

INTERIOR BROWN'S COMPARTMENT
Shooting into corridor as the waiter shakes his head in bewilderment, Ann watching Brown closely.
BROWN: Try the next car. Everybody makes mistakes.
WAITER: *(dubiously)* I guess so.
He exits, Ann pressing back so he can pass. Brown nervously lights a cigarette.
BROWN: *(to Ann)* I'm almost never hungry before noon.
ANN: But you said you could always eat.
BROWN: Not on trains—always eat light. Sandwiches ...
He notices Ann staring out window, plainly disturbed.
BROWN: *(continued)* What's the matter?
ANN: That man on the platform ...
Reverse angle—past Ann and Brown
Shooting through window to platform where Kemp is standing, looking in at them. He turns leisurely away, takes another look over his shoulder, and starts in direction of the station.
ANN: He keeps staring.
BROWN: *(interested)* At you—or both of us?
At this moment Jennings goes by, looking in window.
ANN: Me, mostly. He probably thinks I'm somebody else—funny.
BROWN: Sometimes it's not so funny.
He seems grim and she notices it. Kemp stops again outside telegraph office.
ANN: *(lightly—to Brown)* Well, I'm not going to worry about it. Life's too short.

38

BROWN: *(eyes on Kemp and Jennings)* Yeah, isn't it?
ANN: Which reminds me, I want to get something in the station.
She starts to turn away.
BROWN: *(wire in hand—takes her arm)* Fine, I've got this wire to send . . .
He leads her into corridor, leans back to close door, camera panning to show Mrs. Neil's door open a crack and her tortured face in the gap.
BROWN: *(continued) (for her benefit)* . . . Might even work up an appetite and grab a sandwich . . .
As his door closes, Mrs. Neil's mouth works and we can guess that she's saying "You'd better, you so-and-so."

EXTERIOR LA JUNTA RAILROAD STATION—DAY
Kemp, standing in front of the newsstand next door to the telegraph office, takes a newspaper from the stand, glances at the headlines, then turns, camera panning over to Sam Jennings who is standing on the other side of the telegraph office, gnawing on an apple. The attention of both of them is on the train as Ann and Brown approach.
ANN: *(indicating newsstand)* I think I'll find what I want in there.
BROWN: Go ahead—be with you in a minute.
He pauses at a small sandwich stand as Ann exits into newsstand. Throwing down a coin, he picks up two paper-wrapped sandwiches, stuffs them in his pockets and enters telegraph office.

INTERIOR TELEGRAPH OFFICE—DAY—(PROCESS)
As Brown steps to counter, unfolding his telegraph blank. He lays it down, picks up a pencil, adds a line, then chews on the pencil, trying to make a decision. Yost, reading a newspaper, enters and pauses behind Brown.
YOST: *(sadly)* Ts ts ts.
Brown turns and looks at him.
YOST: *(continued)* Did you see this? *(hands Brown the newspaper)* Insert La Messenger. There is a two-column photo of Forbes' two daughters trying to comfort Mrs. Forbes. In one corner, there is a

small portrait of Forbes. Caption reads: "Widow of Detective--
Sergeant Eben Forbes, Los Angeles policeman slain last night in
Chicago, collapses when told of her husband's murder. With her
are her daughters, Lee (L) and Peggy. (Story Page 2)."
YOST'S VOICE: Sad, isn't it?
Back to scene as Brown finishes reading.
YOST: *(philosophically)* Makes you wish there was something you
could do. *(exits, shaking head)*
Brown tosses aside the newspaper, then comes to his decision. He
begins to cross out part of his message.
Insert telegraph blank. It is addressed to:
> *DISTRICT ATTORNEY—HALL OF JUSTICE*
> *LOS ANGELES*
> *RUN IMMEDIATE FILE ON JOSEPH KEMP,*
> *VINCENT YOST, SAM JENNINGS AND MAN*
> *NAMED DENSEL PLANNING CONTACT EN*
> *ROUTE. OUR CONSIGNMENT SAFE BUT*
> *EXPECT TROUBLE.*
> > > *BROWN*
He crosses out Vincent Yost's name as we read the message.
Back to scene. Brown hands the message to the attendant, opens
his wallet as the other counts the words.
BROWN: Straight wire—urgent.
He manages a look out the window, camera panning to reveal
Jennings watching. The fat man, with a grimace of disgust,
finishes the apple and hurls the core away, then strides off.
ATTENDANT'S VOICE: That'll be one sixty-nine.
New angle as Brown pays him and he hands the telegraph blank
to a girl operator who sits by an electric type transmitter. As he
gives Brown his change, she begins working the machine. Brown,
pocketing his change, quickly exits from the office.

EXTERIOR TELEGRAPH OFFICE—DAY
As Brown comes out, lights a cigarette, and notices Kemp watch-
ing from the front of gift shop. At this moment, Tommy Sinclair,
running ahead of Mrs. Troll, spots Brown and heads him off.
TOMMY: Well, can I see it now?

40

BROWN: *(with a glance toward Kemp)* Son, I'm going to need your help. *(kneels, lowering voice)* I'll bet you can keep a secret, can't you?
TOMMY: I dunno—maybe.
Mrs. Troll enters scene.
BROWN: *(to Mrs. Troll)* It's all right. I'm letting him in on a secret.
MRS. TROLL: I think you'd better come with me, Tommy. You've bothered this man enough.
TOMMY: No. I want to hear it. You buy your magazine.
MRS. TROLL: *(reluctantly)* Very well . . . But we've got to get right back on the train.
She opens her purse, moving off to magazine stand in front of gift shop where Kemp is reading the newspaper. Brown leads Tommy over to a bench in front of telegraph office.

EXTERIOR NEWSSTAND AND GIFT SHOP—DAY
An angle past Kemp as Mrs. Troll selects a magazine; Jennings comes out, stuffing popcorn in his mouth from a paper bag. Camera pans shooting through window of store where we see Ann just paying for a package. She waves to Mrs. Troll as the saleslady makes change. Kemp, folding the paper, walks towards the telegraph office. And now Ann comes out, carrying the package.
ANN: Where's our wandering boy?
MRS. TROLL: I've got him in sight, Mrs. Sinclair. He's talking to his train robber.
She points offstage and Ann reacts.
ANN: *(surprised, smiles)* So that's who it is! *(calls)* Tommy!

EXTERIOR TELEGRAPH OFFICE—DAY
Close on Tommy and Brown on bench as they look towards Ann.
TOMMY: Yes, mother.
He stands up, Brown following.
BROWN: *(puzzled)* Wait a minute—I thought the other lady was your mother.
TOMMY: Nanny? She's my nurse. *(takes Brown's hand)* C'mon, I won't tell 'em anything.
He leads Brown off, camera panning as Ann approaches to meet them, Mrs. Troll entering gift shop. Tommy's eyes go to the package in Ann's hands.

41

He leads Brown off, camera panning as Ann approaches to meet them, Mrs. Troll entering gift shop. Tommy's eyes go to the package in Ann's hands.

ANN: *(to Brown—amiably)* Well, we've solved one of the mysteries about you. They tell me you rob trains for a living.

TOMMY: No, he doesn't—I just thought he did.

ANN: I was ready to believe anything. I'm surprised you don't.

BROWN: *(soberly)* I'm surprised, too. About Tommy being your boy. *(pats Tommy's head—smiles)* He's on my side now, anyway.

TOMMY: We've got a secret. *(indicates package)* Is that for me?

ANN: *(unwrapping package)* Yes, you're going to like this.

She takes out an Indian headdress. Tommy's eyes widen with pleasure.

TOMMY: Gee—an Indian hat!

ANN: That's a genuine headdress, Tommy. A real Indian chief made it.

Tommy puts the headdress on, spotting Mrs. Troll coming out of gift shop.

TOMMY: Thanks, mother. *(starts off)* Hey, look what I've got, Nanny! *(stops, turning to Brown)* Don't forget—nobody knows but us.

BROWN: That's a promise.

Tommy runs over and joins Mrs. Troll, Ann and Brown watching as they move off towards the train.

ANN: You must be very persuasive. A little while ago he was all for having you locked up for armed robbery.

BROWN: That was before he knew I was on a secret mission.

ANN: *(studying him)* I see—that would explain anything, wouldn't it? You're quite inventive.

BROWN: *(anticipating her)* He's a very sensible young man. He didn't press for details.

ANN: In that case I guess I should take a hint.

She is looking at him rather gravely and the lightness has gone from her manner.

BROWN: At least you're one up on me. You know I'm not a train robber—and that's more than I know about you, except that you're married and have a young son.

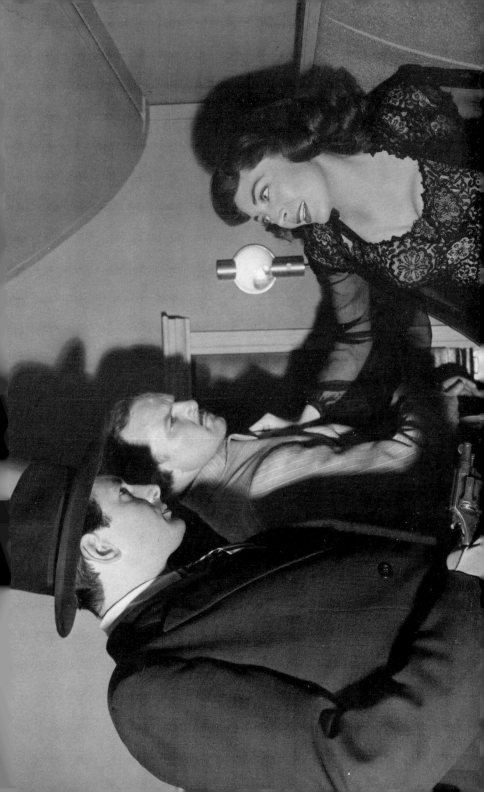

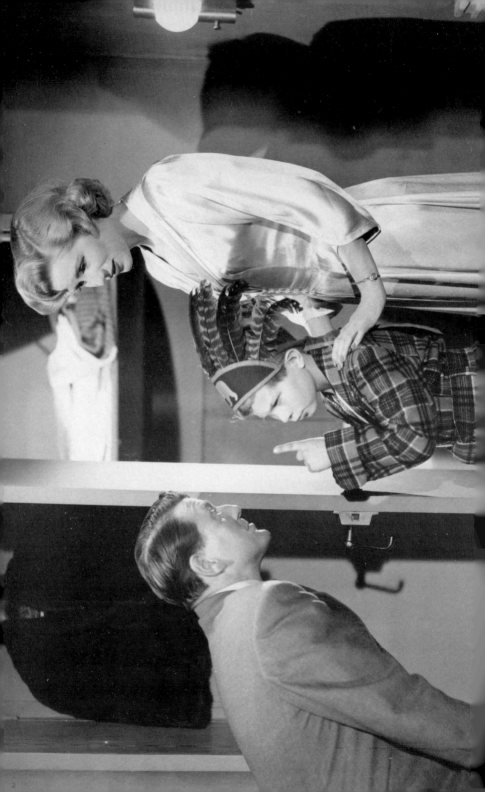

ANN: Is that so unusual?

BROWN: *(troubled)* Not unusual—just unexpected. I didn't figure on it, that's all.

ANN: That sounds like you'd given it some thought. *(smiles)* I didn't think I'd made that much of an impression—but maybe you're like the train. When it's moving, everything's a blur. When it slows down and stops, you begin to notice the scenery.

BROWN: I hadn't thought of it that way, but you're right.

Closeup—Brown as he looks at her appreciatively.

BROWN: Too bad we've got to start moving again.

Closeup—Ann, a little uncomfortable under his scrutiny.

ANN: Yes, we'd better be getting back.

New angle. Brown takes Ann's arm, they walk back toward train. In background, Jennings, who has been watching them, sets a pop bottle down on sandwich stand, ambles after them.

INTERIOR TELEGRAPH OFFICE—DAY

The attendant is giving Kemp some change.

KEMP: Mark it "rush," will you?

ATTENDANT: Yessir.

Camera moves as Kemp turns, looking out window and we can see Ann and Brown moving towards train. There are shouts of "all aboard" and other passengers begin hurrying across plat-form as Kemp crosses to the door and exits, camera tilting down to electric type transmitter as the girl operator works the keys and the following message spells out across the tape:

    MID-WEST EQUIPMENT CO.

    6310 WABASH CHICAGO ILL

    SITUATION CLEARED UP. PARTY USES NAME MRS.

    SINCLAIR. NO SIGN OF DENSEL YET SO WILL

    PROCEED ON MY OWN.

                             KEMP

Blending with the staccato clicking of the typewriter we bring in the sound of a train moving at high speed, gradually building louder until it drowns out the typewriter in a solid roar. As the whistle sounds—

DISSOLVE

INTERIOR CLUB-LOUNGE CAR—DAY

Vestibule—A close shot on Kemp, his face framed against the window and the blur of scenery whizzing past. He appears more composed and determined as though a lot of doubts had been removed. Again his hand reaches under his coat to touch the gun, the feel of which seems to reassure him. He turns his head as the camera pulls back to show Ann entering from next car with Brown. They give him the briefest of glances, passing into the corridor leading to the lounge. Languidly, Kemp withdraws his hand from under coat and follows, still carrying the folded newspaper.

Corridor at glass doors to lounge—Brown holds the door open for Ann, looking back as Kemp appears behind them.

ANN: Aren't you coming in?

BROWN: *(hesitating)* I've got a little business to attend to first—but I'll get back.

ANN: Please don't feel you have to because of me.

BROWN: *(as Kemp squeezes past)* Maybe I *want* to. Because of *you*...

She shrugs, then enters the lounge, camera tilting up to show her cross to a chair and sit down. Kemp sits down opposite her, unfolding the paper to use it as a shield while he keeps his eye on her.

Close shot—Brown observing this. He bites his lip, camera pulling back as he exits back down corridor, almost colliding with Jennings who gives him a dirty look, but makes no move to step aside.

JENNINGS: *(darkly)* It's your turn to make way, my friend.

Brown, without a word, opens the lavatory door, crowds in and lets Jennings squeeze by on his way to the lounge. With the corridor clear, then, Brown continues towards the vestibule.

INTERIOR MRS. NEIL'S COMPARTMENT—DAY

Mrs. Neil, a cigarette between her lips, is lying back on the seat, the portable phonograph open at her side. A record is playing very softly, the same popular tune we heard in the tenement. Suddenly,

44

she sits up at the sound of a door closing in the next compartment. With one quick movement she lifts the arm off the record and shuts the case as Brown's voice is heard outside the connecting door.

BROWN'S VOICE: Come on—open it.

He raps sharply as Mrs. Neil pushes the phonograph case under the seat, steps to the door, unlocking it. Brown quickly enters, shutting the door.

MRS. NEIL: *(angrily)* You sure took your time!

BROWN: What's the idea playing that phonograph? You want 'em to come in here shooting?

MRS. NEIL: I like music.

BROWN: Okay—keep it up, but it won't be long till you're playing something slow and sad.

MRS. NEIL: I'll apologize later. Where's the sandwich?

He pulls a paper-wrapped sandwich from his pocket and she grabs it, sitting down.

BROWN: Take the paper off first.

She peels the paper off. He fishes another sandwich from his other pocket.

MRS. NEIL: *(bites into bread)* Cheese—how thin can a sandwich be?

BROWN: *(divides the other one)* Take half of this. Take it *all!* I can't eat.

He tosses the sandwich into her lap and nervously lights a cigarette.

MRS. NEIL: That's because you've been packing away steaks—behind my back.

BROWN: Oh, stop it—I've got more on my mind than food.

He catches her looking at him slyly as she pops the last of sandwich in her mouth and unwraps the second one.

MRS. NEIL: It wouldn't be the gal who beat me out of my breakfast, would it?

BROWN: You're pretty sharp—only it's not what you think.

MRS. NEIL: *(munching)* It's *exactly* what I think. Why don't you admit you put her on the spot and let me congratulate you?

Brown regards her with surprise.

BROWN: How'd you figure all that out?

45

MRS. NEIL: I heard you through the door. That hood wasn't looking at her big blue eyes. He thinks she's me. And *I* think that's dandy. What's the matter with it?

BROWN: Not a thing—from your standpoint. You're doing fine.

MRS. NEIL: Sure, I'm still breathing. The food stinks, and so does your company, but I'll hand you one thing, Brown, you're beginning to show real genius.

BROWN: Smooth that out a little.

MRS. NEIL: Making this other dame the target shows you're using your head.

BROWN: For your information, I didn't rig it that way.

MRS. NEIL: Baloney! If you didn't, the D.A.'s entitled to a refund.

BROWN: *(disgusted)* Sister, I've known some pretty hard cases in my day, but you make 'em look like putty. You're not talking about a sack of gum drops that'll get smashed—this is a dame's life! You may think it's a funny idea for a woman with a kid to stop a bullet for you, only I'm not laughing.

MRS. NEIL: Where do you get off being so superior? Why shouldn't I take advantage of her? I want to live! If *you* had to step on someone to get something you wanted real bad, would *you* think twice about it?

BROWN: Shut up!

MRS. NEIL: In a pig's eye you would! You're no different from me!

BROWN: Shut up!

    Closer—favoring Mrs. Neil as she stuffs the remainder of the sandwich in her mouth and leaps up, almost choking in rage.

MRS. NEIL: *(blazing)* Not till I tell you something, you cheap badge-pusher! When we started this safari you made it plenty clear I was just a job with no joy in it, remember?

BROWN: Yeah, and it still goes—double!

MRS. NEIL: Okay keep it that way! I don't care whether you dreamed this gag up or not, you're playing right along with it, so don't go soft on me! Once you handed out a line about poor Forbes getting killed because it was his duty. Well, it's *your* duty, too, even if this *dame* gets murdered!

BROWN: You make me sick to my stomach.

MRS. NEIL: The sink's over there!

Brown, without another word, throws down his cigarette, steps on it and exits, slamming the door. Mrs. Neil opens it a crack, camera moving forward to show Brown just reaching for corridor door.

MRS. NEIL: *(nasty sweet)* And let me know when the target practice starts!

He slams the other door and exits. Mrs. Neil closes her door, and bolts it.

INTERIOR CLUB-LOUNGE CAR—DAY

Vestibule—as Brown comes through, hurrying along corridor to glass door at end, camera trucking with him. He stops, his hand on the door, then presses back, looking through glass.

Lounge—shooting past Brown at door. Ann is getting to her feet, starting toward us, and Kemp, folding his newspaper, puts it in his pocket and follows, his expression grim. Camera pulls back as Brown retreats, opens door next to lavatory and goes in. Now Ann comes into scene from lounge, walking down the corridor as Kemp appears at the glass door and slowly opens it, keeping her in sight.

INTERIOR STORE ROOM

A small compartment piled high with supplies for the lounge car, towels, glasses, folding chairs, etc. Brown is at the door holding it open a crack, waiting for Kemp, camera moves forward to shoot past Brown and we see Kemp pass outside in the corridor.

Corridor—reverse angle—as Brown slips out quietly behind Kemp just as Ann disappears around bulge to vestibule. In several long strides Brown catches up to Kemp opposite the man's lavatory and seizes him by the shoulder, spinning him around. His fist connects with Kemp's jaw, the force of the blow knocking Kemp against the lavatory door, which flies open. Both men go through together.

INTERIOR MEN'S LAVATORY (DOUBLE WITH LAVATORY IN PULLMAN)

47

Kemp is spinning backwards against the wash bowls, Brown after him. Before he can swing, Kemp brings his knee up, then slams Brown hard across the face, following through with a sledge-hammer blow to the ribs. Brown stumbles back, landing on the seat, Kemp lunging after him and pouncing. Brown jack-knifes his legs. Kemp goes up—then down, pulling Brown with him to the floor, at the same time fumbling for his gun. The two men, locked together, roll over and over.

Reverse in lavatory as Kemp sprawls under Brown, finally pulling his gun free. Brown's hand clamps down on it and, with the other, he rams Kemp's face against the floor, maneuvering until he has the other pinned down a moment. Both men are breathing heavily, Kemp wincing with pain.

Close shot—on floor as Kemp's hand goes limp, the gun slipping from his fingers. He groans, Brown bringing his foot down on the other's wrist, then reaches for the gun. Before be can touch it, Kemp lifts up. Brown loses his balance, toppling sideways, but managing to kick the gun across the room. Camera pulls back as Kemp lunges for it, Brown scrambling after him. Brown swings at the moment Kemp turns, and the blow sends Kemp spinning across the room to crash against the mirror on the water closet door. The mirror shatters, the door flies open, and Kemp sags into the closet, Brown reaching in to haul him out.

Close at door as the porter opens it, looks in, and quickly exits. Another angle as Brown drags Kemp out of lavatory. Kemp slips to his knees, burying his head in his arms as Brown stands over him, breathing hard. Brown gathers up the gun, leans over and seizes Kemp by the collar.

BROWN: Get up!

Kemp, still keeping his hands over his face, stagger's up and collapses, moaning, on the seat as Brown pockets the gun, pulls down a towel and soaks it in the wash basin.

BROWN: *(continued)* Wash it off with this.

He throws the wet towel at Kemp, who begins swabbing the blood off his face, Brown standing over him.

KEMP: Okay—what was the muscle for? You broke a tooth.

BROWN: You want to try for none? That was just a sample—you're dealing direct with the factory, so you can re-order fast.

Brown's hands are hanging down at his side, Kemp wincing as the hands become fists.

KEMP: No thanks.

BROWN: Let's cut a few corners then. What're you looking for?

KEMP: It might be a briefcase.

BROWN: Come again. Who's the fat guy?

KEMP: I wouldn't know.

BROWN: And Densel—what's he got to do with it?

KEMP: Never heard of him.

Brown clips him a flat-hand blow across the cheek.

BROWN: Hear any better now?

Closer as Kemp glares up at him, his breath coming in short gasps.

KEMP: All right, copper, I'm not in this alone, but *you* are. You're just one guy bucking a big company, and it don't matter if you beat my brains out or not—we're in business for keeps.

BROWN: Quit stalling—talk straight.

KEMP: The pay-off list and the little lady with the little boy—calls herself Mrs. Sinclair. Is that straight enough for you?

BROWN: You're off your stick—way off.

KEMP: Her name's Neil, but the name doesn't matter.

BROWN: It matters plenty, because you're dead wrong.

Kemp looks at him pityingly.

KEMP: *(swabbing face with towel)* Why don't you get wise to yourself and give her a break? What's the use of making that kid an orphan? Or maybe you like trouble.

BROWN: I love it—so get to the point.

KEMP: Give us the list and nobody'll get hurt—no grief, no mess.

BROWN: Except for Mrs. Neil—who gets double-crossed ten minutes later. Don't play me for a jumbo-sized sucker—that list isn't any good as long as she can talk, so make sense!

Kemp gives him an insolent stare, leaving the towel draped around his neck.

KEMP: So you're not going to do business with us?

BROWN: No.

KEMP: You trying to up the price?

BROWN: I don't fix.

KEMP: Check. We get her anyway.

*Brown's hands suddenly close around the towel, drawing it to-
gether like a noose around Kemp's neck, choking off the words, as
Brown squeezes tight and lifts him up.*

BROWN: *(savagely)* You get nobody! Neither the right Mrs. Neil nor
the wrong Mrs. Neil! You get nobody! Where's Densel?

KEMP: *(strangling)* Never heard of him.

*Lifting Kemp bodily, Brown rams him against the bulkhead,
preparatory to knocking his head off.*

BROWN: Who else is covering you? Densel, Yost, the fat man—who
else?

BROWN: *(continued)* How many are with you?

KEMP: *(strangling)* You can't beat it out of me!

BROWN: Talk?

KEMP: No! They'd kill me!

*Lifting Kemp bodily, Brown rams him against the wall and draws
his gun.*

KEMP: *(continued) (frightened)* No!

BROWN: Look at me!

Kemp opens his eyes.

BROWN: *(continued)* If anything happens to her, I'll get to you even
in jail and kill you. *(lets it sink in)* Get up. Stand up! You're under
arrest.

*He backs towards camera motioning Kemp to his feet. Kemp
rises, the towel still around his neck.*

KEMP: This ain't your territory—what's the charge?

BROWN: Soiling towels! C'mon, put your hands behind your neck!
Now waltz over to the window.

Kemp, hands behind neck, steps to window.

*The corridor door opens and the conductor looks in, the fright-
ened porter standing behind him.*

CONDUCTOR: What's going on here?

BROWN: I'm an officer—making a pinch.

CONDUCTOR: *(calls into corridor)* Mr. Jennings, would you step in here a minute?

On Brown's reaction, camera pans to show Sam Jennings as he appears in the door, filling it and looking from Brown to Kemp, then back again.

CONDUCTOR: *(continued)* This man claims he's an officer.

JENNINGS: I'll take over, conductor.

BROWN: On what authority?

JENNINGS: *(shows badge)* Special agent for the railroad. *(to conductor)* We'll handle this. There won't be any trouble.

CONDUCTOR: All right—I'll wire Albuquerque.

He exits with porter as Jennings squeezes in closing door, camera pulling back.

JENNINGS: *(to Brown)* Your credentials won't be necessary, Brown. I checked on you last night. What'll we book him on?

He takes out a pair of handcuffs, crossing to Kemp.

BROWN: Take your choice—concealed weapon, attempted bribe, resisting an officer. I'll want him held in technical custody till the next stop.

Pick up his partner, too. Man named Yost, Vincent Yost—somewhere on board.

JENNINGS: The pleasure's all mine. *(to Kemp)* You can take your hands down now.

Kemp lowers his hands, turning, and Jennings snaps one handcuff over his left wrist, clicking the other around his own. Brown puts his gun away.

BROWN: There'll be a report to make out. Where'll I find you?

JENNINGS: Up front—baggage car.

He starts for the door with Kemp in tow.

BROWN: *(ruefully to Jennings)* I should've tumbled to you before this—flashing that big railroad watch. And talking like a timetable . . .

JENNINGS: *(grins—nudging Kemp)* All right, walk ahead of me, real close—and everybody'll think we're old friends.

51

He opens door for Kemp, who turns to Brown.

KEMP: It's a big company, copper, with branches all over—don't forget that.

As Jennings squeezes through the door behind Kemp, Brown steps to the mirror.

Corridor—towards glass door to lounge as Kemp precedes Jennings to door, both of them stepping aside as a male passenger comes through. Jennings, pressed into bulge of corridor, holds the door for him with his free hand, then follows Kemp into lounge. Opposite end of lounge as Jennings and Kemp approach, continuing past the bar into vestibule leading to next car.

INTERIOR SECOND COMPARTMENT CAR—DAY

Along corridor as Kemp, followed by Jennings, approach camera. A lady passenger hurries in from the other end to meet them midway and stops at sight of Jennings's bulk. A compartment door opens behind Jennings.

JENNINGS: One moment, madame.

He backs up into the open door, Kemp being forced to retrace his steps and keep flat against the bulkhead.

INTERIOR DENSEL'S COMPARTMENT—DAY

Camera pulls back from the doorway and Jennings' broad back to an overcoat with a fur-lined collar, swinging from a hook, and, as the lady passenger squeezes past in the corridor outside, Eddie Densel steps past camera and places the muzzle of a revolver between the fat man's shoulder blades.

DENSEL: *(quietly)* Don't move, Mister . . . !

Densel's free arm goes around Jennings's neck, cutting off his wind.

Corridor as Kemp whirls, sees Densel behind Jennings, and leaps at the fat man, shoving him back into the compartment and following.

INTERIOR COMPARTMENT—DAY

Densel, his arm hooked around Jennings' neck, still holds the gun in his back as Kemp kicks the door shut. Densel is favoring his left arm and seems to be experiencing some pain as he holds the gun in the detective's back.

DENSEL: Get his keys—the gun!

Kemp nods, goes through Jennings' pockets and pulls out the key chain, quickly unlocking first one handcuff, then removing the fat man's gun. Jennings, eyes popping, is still helpless in Densel's grip, unable to make an outcry. As Densel twists the gun to use the muzzle as a handle and raises it, camera pans to Kemp who is unlocking the other handcuff. There is the sound of a blow, a grunt and Jennings falls into frame at Kemp's feet, face forward, still groaning faintly.

KEMP: *(rubbing wrist)* I'd about given you up, Densel. I didn't see you get on back there.

Densel, stepping over Jennings, enters lavatory.

DENSEL: Nobody else did, either, which is lucky for you. *(winces)* Take care of him, I got nicked in the shoulder . . .

He emerges with a towel, flops Jennings over with his foot, and kneels, stuffing a handkerchief in the detective's mouth.

KEMP: Brown threw the hook. He ain't on the take.

DENSEL: Who needs him? *I'm* here now.

KEMP: You tell Yost?

DENSEL: *(nods)* I put him off at La Junta.

Kemp twists Jennings' arm behind his back, takes the cuffs and locks the fat man's wrists together as Densel secures the gag with the towel, camera panning to window and the blur of scenery speeding past outside the glass.

EXTERIOR TRAIN—DAY
The streamliner rocketing across a high trestle, banking off into a narrow cut of mountains as the camera follows in a fast pan.

INTERIOR MRS. NEIL'S COMPARTMENT—DAY
She is just opening the door. Brown stands in the doorway, swabbing at a cut on his chin with a towel. His tie is twisted and his face shows unmistakable signs of battle.

MRS. NEIL: Say, you look pretty! What've you been doing, falling off the train?

BROWN: *(still in doorway)* Yeah, off and on. I tangled with one of your chums—the one that figured the other gal was you. He's cooling off in the baggage car with a pair of handcuffs.

MRS. NEIL: What was his top bid?

BROWN: Whose?

MRS. NEIL: *(craftily)* Don't play dumb with me, Brown! You want to get your hands on that list, because you've got a cash customer for it—that hood! Am I right?

BROWN: *Half* right. You're a good judge of crooks, Mrs. Neil—the only place you slip up is with cops. I turned the deal down.

MRS. NEIL: *(jumps up)* Then you're a bigger idiot than I thought! When'll you get it through your square head that this is big business—and that we're in the middle?

BROWN: Meaning you'd like to sell out?

MRS. NEIL: *(heatedly)* With pleasure and profit—and so would you! What're the odds if we don't? I sing my song for the grand jury—and spend the rest of my life dodging bullets, if I'm *lucky,* while you grow old and gray on the police force! Wake up Brown, this train's headed straight for the cemetery, but there's another one coming along—the *gravy* train! Let's get on it!

BROWN: *(quietly)* Mrs. Neil, I'd like to give you the same answer I gave that hood, but it would mean stepping on your face.

MRS. NEIL: Are you trying to say it's no deal?

BROWN: *(ominously)* I just said it—without the trimmings. If you want those, keep talking!

Abruptly, he turns away, opens connecting door and exits, Mrs. Neil sitting down. She strikes a match, puts a cigarette in her mouth, and lights it, leaning back with a trace of a smile on her lips.

DISSOLVE

EXTERIOR NEW MEXICO LANDSCAPE—NIGHT
A slow pan shot from a high elevation to follow the twinkling ribbon of lights of the streamliner moving across a deep valley. Superimposed over this a strip of telegraph tape begins spinning, spelling out the following message:

WALTER BROWN GOLDEN WEST LIMITED EN-
ROUTE ALBUQUERQUE ... DENSEL AND KEMP
BOTH DANGEROUS GUNMEN MEMBERS SYNDI-
CATE INVOLVED THIS CASE.
DENSEL LAST REPORTED LEAVING CHICAGO BY
PLANE ... WITWER ...

DISSOLVE

INTERIOR PULLMAN CORRIDOR—NIGHT
*Brown, having just finished reading the wire, tears it up, stuffing
the pieces in the dispenser next to the water cooler. He starts off,
then turns, his eyes on something out the window. He bends
closer, frowns.*
CONDUCTOR: *(calling)* Mr. Brown—!
Brown turns, the conductor hurrying up to him.
CONDUCTOR: *(continued)* You haven't seen Mr. Jennings, have you?
BROWN: No—what's wrong?
CONDUCTOR: The crew hasn't seen him, either. He's not up front—
and there's no sign of his prisoner. They're both gone.
BROWN: All right, this rattler hasn't stopped—they're still on it.
*He starts back along corridor, the conductor leading. Again his
gaze goes out the window. He pauses, shrugs, then hurries after
conductor as the camera swings into window and we see the
highway outside, bordering the track—a narrow band of concrete
snaking along the roadbed and a big car racing abreast of the
train at terrific speed, its headlights cutting the darkness.*

EXTERIOR NEW MEXICO LANDSCAPE—NIGHT
*High camera over track. The streamliner zooms toward us, the
headlight boring into the camera. To the left, bounding along the
highway, comes the car and as the train whips out of sight
beneath, camera tilts down to pick up the car banking into a turn
which leads under a small bridge supporting the track. The car
emerges on the other side of the track and races on abreast of the
train.*

INTERIOR BAGGAGE CAR

Shooting through open sliding door—a full shot of the highway and the car racing alongside the train. Camera pulls back and we see Brown inside, watching the highway. To one side, near a desk, stand the brakeman, the conductor and an assistant, who holds a passenger list ... The conductor takes it.

CONDUCTOR: *(coming over)* We picked up four at La Junta. *(shows him list)* Two sections and one compartment.

BROWN: The compartment interests me—but you'd better go through the whole train.

His glance goes back to the door and he leans forward for another look, motioning the conductor over.

BROWN: *(continued)* See that car?

The conductor peers out.

CONDUCTOR: Really moving, isn't he?

BROWN: *(worried)* He's been with us for some time now. *(straightens)* I want you to get a message off—to the highway patrol. *(as the conductor opens book to write)* Black sedan pacing train five—the Golden West Limited. Tell 'em where we are and have 'em intercept that car. *(moves toward rear)* Be right with you. I want a word with Mrs. Sinclair.

He exits through steel door at end of baggage car, camera moving with Conductor, who finishes scribbling and rips a page from his book, handing it to the brakeman.

CONDUCTOR: Drop this off at Cerillo.

The brakeman nods, taking down a hoop from a rack over desk, as the Conductor and assistant go through steel door.

EXTERIOR CERILLO JUNCTION—NIGHT

The streamliner is pounding along the track toward camera. The whistle sounds two short blasts and the dispatcher, hurrying from the shack with a long hooked pole, takes up a position at edge of platform. As the train whisks past, he raises the pole, the hook engaging the hoop on the side of baggage car. As the train thunders out of scene, the dispatcher unties the message from the hoop, walking back into shack.

56

Wide angle traveling camera ahead of the streamliner to include the road curving with the track and the car speeding towards us. Now the track veers away from the road. The train shoots off to the right away from the highway, the coaches banking to the grade, forming a chain of lights which sweep past in a long bending arc away from the car.

INTERIOR TRAIN—NIGHT
Corridor outside Ann's compartment as Brown enters, pressing the buzzer on her door. He is in a state of agitation, shooting nervous glances up and down the corridor. Then Ann opens the door.
ANN: Well—won't you come in?
BROWN: If you can spare a minute.
She steps aside, Brown entering.
ANN: Of course.

INTERIOR ANN'S COMPARTMENT—NIGHT
The sofa has been made into a bed, Ann's overnight bag is open on the cover, and it is apparent she was getting ready to retire. As Brown enters, Ann indicates the lounge chair, crossing to the bed.
ANN: You have a choice of one chair.
Brown pulls the chair into position, facing the bed.
BROWN: *(reaching in pocket)* Thanks—and I'll borrow a cigarette, if you don't mind. I seem to be out of everything.
She hands him a pack, aware of his tension, and watches him as he lights a cigarette, still standing.
ANN: Everything but the jitters—I see they're back again. Maybe this big secret you're carrying around is too much for you.
Brown gives her a sharp look, flicking the match into the tray.
BROWN: *(pulls chair closer)* Mrs. Sinclair, it's the secret I came to talk to you about . . .
New angle reverse—as Ann sits down on bed.
ANN: I feel like I'm intruding on your conspiracy. After all, whatever this is, it's between you and Tommy.
BROWN: Not quite. You're in it, too, but I wish you weren't.

He sits on the edge of the chair, facing her nervously smoking as Ann studies him.

ANN: I think you're serious.

BROWN: I am. You've heard of innocent bystanders getting hit by cars or bullets when it wasn't any of their affair—well, it's one of those things. You're an innocent bystander.

He reaches over, flicking ashes in the tray.

ANN: But nothing's hit me—or is it you're afraid something will?

BROWN: That's the general idea.

ANN: And it might be a bullet.

BROWN: *(nods)* It could be anything. The point is, you've been mistaken for somebody else—and that somebody's not popular. Nothing's going to happen to you, because in a way this is my fault, and I'll *see* that it doesn't. But I want to put you on your guard . . .

He crushes out the cigarette, Ann staring at him a little stunned and frightened.

BROWN: *(continued) (ill at ease)* It'll work out all right.

ANN: I'm not so sure.

BROWN: Will it help any if I tell you I'm a detective—and that this is everyday business with me?

Ann stares at him a moment as though weighing this.

ANN: It would help if you told me the truth, Mr. Brown—which you haven't.

BROWN: *(uncomfortably)* You're right—but it wasn't easy telling you this much.

He looks off, camera panning as they notice the connecting door opening a crack. Tommy slowly opens it the rest of the way and stands there in his pajamas, wearing the Indian headdress.

BROWN: *(continued)* Oh, hello, Tommy.

TOMMY: *(seriously)* You're not going to tell her our secret, are you?

BROWN: I may have to.

ANN: *(getting up)* Little boys have big ears—and this one has a long memory.

She crosses and takes Tommy's hand.

BROWN: I think your mother can keep a secret, Tommy. Shall we try her out?

TOMMY: All right, if you say so, but nobody else.

ANN: *(opening door)* It's bedtime. Come on now. *(to Brown)* Excuse me a minute.

She goes into next compartment, Tommy hanging back a moment.

TOMMY: *(to Brown)* If you need me, just knock on the door.

BROWN: Okay, son, I won't let you down. Sleep tight.

Tommy exits into next compartment, Brown turning to look out the window again, his expression more worried than ever.

INTERIOR CORRIDOR BROWN'S COMPARTMENT CAR

As Densel, followed by Kemp, enter scene.

DENSEL: *(stopping at door)* This the cop's compartment?

KEMP: Yeah, but I already looked there.

DENSEL: That was yesterday—and I still want that list.

He glances up and down corridor, then opens the door, entering with Kemp.

INTERIOR BROWN'S COMPARTMENT—NIGHT

Densel and Kemp enter quietly, looking around. Faintly, coming from the adjoining compartment, they hear phonograph music. As Kemp closes the corridor door, Densel touches his arm, jerking a finger toward Mrs. Neil's door.

DENSEL: *(whispers)* I thought you said nobody was in there . . .

Kemp, puzzled, listens a moment, stepping over to the door.

INTERIOR MRS. NEIL'S COMPARTMENT

Mrs. Neil has apparently heard them enter next door, because she is already getting to her feet and shutting off the phonograph, which she slides under the seat—straightening as there is a short rap on the connecting door.

MRS. NEIL: *(guardedly)* Who is it?

Her hand goes to the catch, but she doesn't open it.

INTERIOR BROWN'S COMPARTMENT

Close shot—Densel and Kemp at connecting door. They look at each other, perplexed. Kemp shrugs helplessly, Densel's face setting in a hard smile.

59

DENSEL: *(raps again)* It's Brown—Lemme in . . .
> *Closer at door. The catch slips and the door opens a crack, Mrs. Neil getting a flash of the two men.*

MRS. NEIL: *(slamming door)* Like fun it is!
> *Densel's knee rams the door as Mrs. Neil hurls her weight against it, trying to slip the catch. Kemp stands back and butts his shoulder against the door and it flies open, Densel entering with his gun drawn.*

INTERIOR MRS. NEIL'S COMPARTMENT
> *The blow on the door has pitched her back into the seat, and she is just scrambling up as the two men come in.*

MRS. NEIL: *(explosively)* You've got a nerve barging in here! What's the idea?
> *She makes a lunge for the connecting door, but Kemp cracks her across the face with his hand and she staggers back, almost falling on the seat.*

KEMP: Where d' you think you're going?
> *New angle. Densel's eyes are flicking around the room. He closes the connecting door, Mrs. Neil holding her cheek.*

DENSEL: *(quietly)* Sit down—and don't make any noise.
> *Closer shot—favoring Mrs. Neil. She looks at the two men, then at the gun, and some of the fire goes out of her.*

MRS. NEIL: *(coolly)* All right, boys. I guess it's time for a showdown . . . So before you make any mistakes let me—
> *Densel gives her a light push and her legs hit the seat. She sits down. He comes closer.*

DENSEL: *(to Kemp)* She's been in here all the time. The cop was too smart for you.

MRS. NEIL: That's where you're mixed up.

DENSEL: *(sharply)* Who asked you?

KEMP: *(grimly)* I guess I got my lines crossed.

DENSEL: *(to Mrs. Neil)* Where's the pay-off list?

MRS. NEIL: That's what I'm trying to tell you. I haven't got it. I—
> *Kemp seizes her wrist, twists it.*

KEMP: Has Brown got it? Hurry up—tell us!

Mrs. Neil doesn't flinch. Kemp twists a little more and she fights back an impulse to cry out.

MRS. NEIL: *(clenching teeth)* Go ahead, break it—you still won't get what you're looking for!

DENSEL: Why not?

MRS. NEIL: *(to Densel)* Tell this muzzler to let go of me and I'll show you!

Wider angle. Densel nods to Kemp, who drops her wrist, Mrs. Neil getting up rapidly, glaring at both men.

MRS. NEIL: You had it all figured out, didn't you? Well, you're wrong . . . !

She steps purposely over to the wardrobe, opens it and reaches for her coat, turning her back as Densel picks up a pillow and holds it over the muzzle of his revolver

MRS. NEIL: *(continued)* I'm— *(she turns, horrified)* Wait—please! *Her scream is drowned out by the muffled report of the gun. Close at wardrobe. Mrs. Neil sags and falls forward, landing heavily on the floor, camera pulling back as Densel puts the gun away, Kemp dragging a suitcase from the seat. Densel yanks the phonograph case out, opens it on the seat.*

KEMP: I went through the cop's stuff.

DENSEL: We'll go through it again. I don't want to miss any bets . . . *He looks over top of phonograph case as he opens lid, then raises the shade, camera moving forward to shoot toward window. The sedan is holding its own, roaring along parallel to the track.*

KEMP'S VOICE: That it?

DENSEL'S VOICE: Yeah—holding his own, too. It won't be so easy to make contact on the grade, so hurry up.

EXTERIOR ANN'S COMPARTMENT

Shooting through window. Brown, nervously smoking, straightens from the window across the glass of which we see the reflected image of the sedan and the highway. Ann is just coming in from the connecting compartment.

INTERIOR ANN'S COMPARTMENT

61

Ann closes the connecting door, looks at Brown.

BROWN: I guess I'd better level with you. I've got an important witness on my hands and she's got a lot of enemies. I don't suppose you've heard of her, but she was married to a gangster who got killed. Frankie Neil.

ANN: *(a little bitterly)* I've heard of her.

Ann gets up and regards him with sudden anger.

BROWN: Now don't lose your nerve—just trust me, will you?

ANN: Not particularly. What would you say if I told you *I'm* Mrs. Neil?

BROWN: *(stunned)* You're—*what?*

ANN: I'm Frank Neil's widow, Mr. Brown! Now do you see what you've done?

Brown's hand goes to his head. He's trying to clear his mind.

BROWN: *(dazed)* But you couldn't be! The D.A. would've told me . . . !

ANN: *(hotly)* Obviously he didn't—but he told me to get to the coast and attract as little attention as possible. Well, it hasn't worked out that way . . . !

BROWN: Then who've I got back there in the compartment?

ANN: A police woman. From—I think they called it the Internal Affairs Division.

BROWN: Played for a sucker! But why? Why stick *me* with a decoy?

ANN: They've been testing you. There's a grand jury investigation of graft and pay-offs, remember?

BROWN: *(indignant)* I never took a bribe in my life!

ANN: Maybe your price was never met.

BROWN: Never was and never could be. I don't say I've never been tempted. I'm human—I can be tempted. But to spend the rest of my time worrying when I'll be caught up with, to give some hoodlum a first mortgage on my life, payable on demand—*(shakes his head)*—what amount of money is worth that? That's what it always boils down to. My record's clean. The Internal Affairs Division knows it.

ANN: Maybe with the way things are, they can never be sure. When I married Frankie Neil, I was pretty sure of him, too. Then I found out how he made his money and I left him. I only saw him once again before he was killed. The pay-off list was in his things . . .

BROWN: You'd better let me have it.

ANN: I couldn't if I wanted to. I mailed it to the district attorney.

BROWN: *(stares at her thoughtfully)* Funny thing. I once asked my partner Forbes, who was killed, what kind of a woman would marry a hoodlum, and he said *all* kinds. I didn't believe him then, but he was right.

They both turn as the buzzer sounds on the corridor door, Brown wheeling and motioning her back as he steps over to it and draws his gun.

BROWN: *(continued) (tensely)* Who is it?

CONDUCTOR'S VOICE: The conductor—may I see you a moment, Mr. Brown?

Camera moving forward as Brown opens the door and we see the conductor standing outside in the corridor. Brown puts the gun away.

CONDUCTOR: *(with a glance at Ann)* Privately, if I can.

BROWN: *(turns to Ann)* I'll get you there all right—don't worry. But keep your door locked.

He steps into corridor as Ann locks the door behind him.

EXTERIOR ANN'S COMPARTMENT—NIGHT
Shooting through window as we see her turn from the door. Reflected in the glass is the image of the highway and the car pacing the train.

SWING WIPE

EXTERIOR BROWN'S COMPARTMENT—NIGHT .
Shooting at drawn blind on window. The car creeps into scene on the dark glass, clearly visible in the reflection; then the shade is raised and we see Densel peering out, his face a mask. He looks at his watch.

INTERIOR BROWN'S COMPARTMENT—NIGHT
Densel turns away from window, camera pulling back to show connecting door open and Kemp in the adjoining compartment. Both rooms have been thoroughly ransacked. Suitcases lie open

on the floor, their contents strewn in all directions, and even the upholstery on the seats shows evidence of having been cut open with a knife. Densel enters Mrs. Neil's compartment.

INTERIOR MRS. NEIL'S COMPARTMENT—NIGHT
Kemp, who has been slashing the upholstery on the berth seat, suddenly reaches down behind it, grabs something.

KEMP: *(his back to Densel)* Well, what d'you know? *(he turns, holding an object in his hand)* I was right the first time.

He opens his hand, palming a small leather folder, with an identification card on one side and a police badge on the other. Insert leather folder in Kemp's hand:

The card reads:

IDENTIFICATION
Police woman Sarah Meggs of the City of Chicago, Cook County, Ill.

The badge bears the insignia of the Chicago Police Department.

DENSEL'S VOICE: A police woman.

Back to scene as Kemp grins, his triumph evident.

DENSEL: *(glances down at body—then at Kemp)* My apologies to both of you. *(grimly)* Now let's get the real Mrs. Neil. Where is she?

KEMP: Up ahead—a pair of rooms. C and D.

DENSEL: We'll button it up fast.

He throws another glance at window as Kemp tosses the folder away. They are already moving for the connecting door.

EXTERIOR MRS. NEIL'S COMPARTMENT
Shooting through window as the two men exit into Brown's compartment.

SWING WIPE

EXTERIOR DENSEL'S COMPARTMENT—NIGHT
Shooting through window. Inside, Jennings is standing with the brakeman, who is just removing the handcuffs.

INTERIOR DENSEL'S COMPARTMENT
Towards door as Brown enters with the conductor.
BROWN: I heard what happened. Who was the second guy?
JENNINGS: I don't know. He didn't leave his calling card. *(points off)*
Only that coat.
Camera swings to bulkhead as Brown whirls and spots the overcoat with the fur-lined collar.
BROWN: *(grimly)* That's his calling card. C'mon ...!
He exits out quickly, the conductor following with Jennings, who pauses in door, turning to brakeman.
JENNINGS: I'll borrow your gun.
The brakeman pulls out a revolver, Jennings shoving it in his pocket and exiting.

INTERIOR CORRIDOR OUTSIDE ANN'S COMPARTMENT
Densel and Kemp enter, the latter indicating Ann's door. Densel nods, glances at watch.
DENSEL: I'll handle this end—go ahead.
Kemp nods, hurrying into vestibule as Densel steps over to Ann's door, drawing his gun. Slowly he turns the door handle, finds it's locked.

INTERIOR ANN'S COMPARTMENT—NIGHT
She gets to her feet from the berth, her eyes wide with fear, as the camera zooms in on the doorknob twisting slowly back and forth.
DENSEL'S VOICE: Open the door, Mrs. Neil.
Closeup—Ann. Her hand goes to her throat and she remains standing, frozen, waiting in silence.
Vestibule—as Kemp hurries through to another car.
Corridor—close on Densel. He debates blowing the lock off with the gun, then moves to the adjoining compartment, camera pulling back as he tries this handle, finds it locked, then knocks softly.

INTERIOR ADJOINING COMPARTMENT—NIGHT

65

*Tommy sits up in bed, jumps to the floor and turns on the light.
The knock is repeated, Mrs. Troll pulling herself upright in the
berth above.*

MRS. TROLL: *(in a frightened whisper)* Tommy . . . ! What is it?
*Before she can stop him, Tommy has put on his Indian headdress
and crossed to the door.*

TOMMY: *(confidently)* It's all right—I know who it is . . .
*He reaches for the door catch, turns it.
Corridor. Densel waits until the catch slips, then enters quickly.*

INTERIOR TOMMY'S COMPARTMENT—NIGHT
*As Densel enters, shutting door. Tommy backs away, but Densel
grabs him by the arm, Mrs. Troll reacting in alarm.*

TOMMY: *(struggling)* Let go of me! Let me go . . . !

MRS. TROLL: What're you doing? Let him go!
*Densel holding Tommy, drags him to connecting door and
knocks.*

DENSEL: You'd better open it, Mrs. Neil!

INTERIOR ANN'S COMPARTMENT—NIGHT
Ann turns from corridor door, starts for connecting door.

ANN: Tommy . . . !

TOMMY'S VOICE: Don't open it, mother—he's got a gun!
She hesitates, her face a mask of horror.

DENSEL'S VOICE: It's your kid—hurry up!
Making a quick decision, she reaches for the catch.

INTERIOR VESTIBULE—SEVERAL CARS BACK IN
TRAIN
*Kemp glances at his watch, then reaches up for the airbrakes
emergency lever, a metal handle attached to a short cord. He
yanks it and immediately there is a hiss of air and a shriek of
grabbing brakes. The floor bucks under him.*

INTERIOR ANN'S COMPARTMENT—NIGHT
*Ann falls back as the door, unlocked now, flies open, Densel
staggering in as the force of gravity flops over a chair and the*

66

*lavatory door bangs open. He shoves Tommy back into the other
compartment, slams the door and bolts it, Ann almost losing her
balance as she comes up hard against the opposite bulkhead.*
DENSEL: *(turns, steadying himself)* Where's the list, Mrs. Neil?
ANN: *(pressed against bulkhead)* I—I haven't got it.
Densel starts for her.

INTERIOR CORRIDOR—NIGHT
*Brown, followed by the conductor and Jennings, pounds into
scene as Tommy's compartment door opens, Mrs. Troll coming
out in a wild state of excitement.*
MRS. TROLL: *(terrified)* He's got her in there—with a gun!
*Brown shoves past into compartment with conductor, Jennings
stepping to the corridor door of Ann's compartment.*

INTERIOR TOMMY'S COMPARTMENT—NIGHT
*Brown entering with conductor as Tommy pounds on the con-
necting door. Brown lifts him aside.*
TOMMY: It's a real train robber . . . ! He's locked the door!
BROWN: *(rapping)* You in there—we've got you covered on both
sides, here and the corridor! Open this door or *we'll* open it and come
in shooting!
*The conductor hands Brown some keys, one of which Brown
inserts in the lock.*

INTERIOR ANN'S COMPARTMENT—NIGHT
*Densel turns from Ann, steps to side of connecting door, as the key
rattles in the lock.*
DENSEL: Listen, copper, the first door that opens I'll put a bullet
through this dame's head! *(to Ann)* Give me the list, Mrs. Neil, and I
might give you a break.
*The train shudders to a complete stop, camera panning to win-
dow as we see another train on the siding next to us—the
darkened windows of a pullman. Over shot we hear a sighing of
airbrakes and a last clattering bang from the couplings.*

INTERIOR TOMMY'S COMPARTMENT—NIGHT

Shooting past Brown through windows at Pullman Car opposite. Ann's compartment is reflected in the glass, the figures of Ann and Densel clearly visible to Brown, who is beginning to get an idea. He suddenly clicks off the light in his compartment, camera panning as he raps on door, his gaze wandering to window.

BROWN: Ann—listen to me! He knows you've got that list! *(hammering the point)* You're in a bad spot—there's no use holding out on him!

INTERIOR ANN'S COMPARTMENT—NIGHT
Densel straightens from Ann, glances towards connecting door.

DENSEL: *(to Ann)* The cop's right—come on—hand it over!

BROWN'S VOICE: Play ball with him. Do what he tells you.

Close shot—Ann, as she realizes Brown is pulling a ruse, now plays along.

ANN: All right ... I'll get it for you.

INTERIOR TOMMY'S COMPARTMENT—NIGHT
Shooting past Brown. Reflected in the other car's window we see Ann stoop over and begin rummaging through her suitcase. Brown stepping to connecting door, gun drawn with a bead on Densel. Before he can fire, Densel moves out of range. Brown is on the point of firing through door but stops as Ann moves in front of Densel. Brown lowers the gun.

INTERIOR ANN'S COMPARTMENT—NIGHT
Densel peers out the window.

DENSEL: *(turning to Ann)* Quit stalling!

BROWN'S VOICE: Ann—we can't help you. Don't stall him. Get him the list—*in the medicine cabinet!*

DENSEL: The medicine cabinet—!

Abruptly he shoves Ann aside, moves eagerly toward lavatory.

INTERIOR TOMMY'S COMPARTMENT—NIGHT
Shooting past Brown into reflection of other car window, as Densel steps in front of door.

Closeup—Brown. He looks at reflection, measures the chances, then fires through the door—three times.

INTERIOR ANN'S COMPARTMENT—NIGHT
Densel staggers back, clutching his left wrist which is bleeding. He drops the gun, leaps for the door (which has three holes through it) and manages to jam his foot against the bottom just as Brown shoves hard from the other side. Densel's eyes dart around for an escape. He picks up a heavy floor ash tray with his good hand, swings it against the window, cracks the glass out, still keeping one foot against the door, his legs spread wide apart.
Close on floor. The gun. Camera tilts up as Ann starts for it. Densel beats her to it, pulling it towards him with his foot and back-handing her aside. Then he steps back, whirling as the door flies open behind him. He brings the gun up to fire.
Reverse angle. Brown comes through the door fast, firing twice. Densel stumbles back, supporting himself on the bulkhead. His jaw sags and he suddenly collapses backwards on the berth, slides off and lands on the floor, face down. The conductor enters. Ann sits down in the chair and begins sobbing as Tommy rushes in and clings to her.
BROWN: *(to conductor)* Take over here.
Brown opens the corridor door, camera moving forward to reveal Jennings outside with a revolver in his hand. Over shot the siren noise grows louder.

INTERIOR CORRIDOR
As Brown comes out, motioning to Jennings. The car jolts forward, camera panning to window as Brown and Jennings rush towards vestibule and we see the shadowy outlines of a water tower moving past as the train begins moving.

EXTERIOR TRAIN—NIGHT
Panning shot towards last car as Kemp, waiting in the open door of the vestibule, drops to the track and begins running back along the roadbed as the train travels past. The siren noise is building.

69

INTERIOR TRAIN—NIGHT
Vestibule as Brown and Jennings race through to the next car.

EXTERIOR OBSERVATION CAR—NIGHT
At railing—shooting back towards junction as the track unwinds behind us and we see Kemp running towards the getaway car, the lights of which are dancing over the rough roadbed parallel to the track, overtaking the train. Brown and Jennings enter scene, stepping to the rail at the exact moment the car stops and Kemp jumps in. The driver jams the car in gear and it veers to cross the track, then pulls up abruptly as a highway patrol car spins into scene from behind the other train on the siding. A spotlight illuminates the getaway car, which begins to back up across the track. Another highway patrol car roars in from behind the water tower, the officers of both cars leaping out with drawn guns as the getaway car, hemmed in on both sides, stops, Kemp and the driver alighting to raise their hands in surrender—the figures of police and captives growing ever smaller as the train gathers speed, camera pulling back to show Brown putting away his gun and turning, the lights of the cars making a faint glow in the distance. As Jennings follows Brown through door into car past camera, we—

DISSOLVE

EXTERIOR LOS ANGELES UNION STATION—DAY
High camera over the multiple tracks leading into the station proper as the streamliner rolls slowly towards us past long lines of box cars, pullmans and railroad equipment in the sprawling yards.

DISSOLVE

INTERIOR RAILROAD PLATFORM—DAY
The streamliner is moving slowly towards us and we see a waiting throng fan out to meet the coaches and, in the distance, a group of

newspaper reporters and photographers break into a run for the compartment cars. With a wheezing of airbrakes the train stops. Reverse angle at vestibule of compartment car. The reporters are impatiently waiting to get aboard as the conductor gets off with the porter, the latter assisting some passengers to alight.

1ST REPORTER: *(to conductor)* We're looking for a certain lady, conductor—a Mrs. Neil. This her car?

CONDUCTOR: I wouldn't know.

2ND REPORTER: She's with a cop—a guy named Brown. Where do we find 'em?

CONDUCTOR: I'm sorry, I can't answer that.

1ST REPORTER: It's all right—he's expecting us. *(to others)* Let's go. *The reporters pile aboard the car, followed by photographers carrying cameras.*

INTERIOR TRAIN—DAY
Ann's compartment at window, as Brown turns from glass, camera pulling back to reveal Jennings as he helps Ann into her coat. Through the connecting door Tommy and Mrs. Troll are getting ready in the adjoining compartment.

BROWN: They're on to us.

ANN: Reporters?

BROWN: *(nods)* The works—cameras, too. *(to Jennings)* How do we beat this rap?

JENNINGS: *(chuckles)* By size alone. Follow me. *He motions Ann into next compartment, Brown following as the buzzer sounds on the corridor door.*

REPORTERS: *(offstage)* Mrs. Neil, can we see you a minute? All we want's a statement what you're going to tell the Grand Jury! What about that pay-off list, Mrs. Neil?

JENNINGS: *(calls off)* She's not quite ready, boys. *He waddles into next compartment, closing the door.*

INTERIOR TOMMY'S COMPARTMENT
As Jennings comes through, crossing to corridor door.

ANN: *(to Mrs. Troll)* Take Tommy with you, Mrs. Troll . . . I'll meet you at the hotel.

71

MRS. TROLL: Yes, Miss Ann.

ANN: *(to Tommy)* Goodbye, darling—I'll see you later.

TOMMY: *(to Brown)* You think you'll get away from 'em?

BROWN: I don't know—they're on the warpath. It's up to the big chief here.

JENNINGS: *(slips door catch)* I'll go first, Brown—the rest is your department. *(shakes hands)* Good luck—and take care of yourself, Mrs. Neil.

BROWN: *(grins)* That's my department, too. Much obliged.

ANN: Thanks for everything, Mr. Jennings.

JENNINGS: Here we go.

> *He swings the corridor door open and squeezes through, stepping back to allow Ann and Brown to hurry out.*
>
> *Corridor—shooting past Jennings as Ann and Brown come out behind him, racing off down the passage as the camera trucks the other way with the fat man who lumbers up against the reporters, bunched in front of Ann's door.*

JENNINGS: *(butting into them)* Gangway, boys, you're blocking traffic.

REPORTERS: *(being pushed along)* Hey—what's the idea, man mountain? We've got business here! Hold it, Mister—what're you trying to do, keep an elephant out of a job?

> *As Jennings reaches the bulge at the end of the passage, the reporters squeeze past him, rushing back to Ann's door.*

JENNINGS: *(turns, swabs brow)* Like I always say—nobody loves a fat man.

EXTERIOR RAILROAD PLATFORM—DAY

> *At entrance to ramp—as Brown approaches with Ann. Two plainclothes officers move to meet them.*

BROWN: Hello, Allan—everything under control?

1ST OFFICER: *(nods)* Got a car waiting—the D.A.'s waiting and there's a big crowd out front, waiting. *(takes Ann's arm)* We'll get you out the side way, Mrs. Neil, and they won't see you.

> *They enter ramp.*

INTERIOR RAMP—DAY

Begin dolly shot as the group starts down ramp.

ANN: *(thoughtfully)* But they'll *have* to see me sometime. *(to Brown)* Did it ever occur to you I can't keep running and hiding all my life?

BROWN: Right now it's kind of a safe idea.

ANN: *(shakes her head)* No—right now is a good time to stop. Where is it we're going?

They stop at bottom of ramp—at entrance to tunnel.

BROWN: Hall of Justice—couple of blocks.

ANN: Then these gentlemen will have to excuse us—we're going to walk.

Brown takes her hand and they start along tunnel. The two officers look at each other helplessly.

BROWN: *(smiles—turning)* You heard what the lady said, boys.

They hurry along tunnel together, the camera panning as they exit off and we—

FADE OUT

THE END